SADLIER

VOCABULARY WORKSHOP®

ACHIEVE

Level G

Jerome Shostak

Senior Series Consultant

Vicki A. Jacobs, Ed.D.
Director, Teacher Education Program
Harvard Graduate School of Education
Cambridge, Massachusetts

Series Consultants

Louis P. De Angelo, Ed.D.
Superintendent of Schools
Diocese of Wilmington
Wilmington, Delaware

John Heath, Ph.D.
Professor of Classics
Santa Clara University
Santa Clara, California

Sarah Ressler Wright, M.A. English Ed, NBCT
Head Librarian
Rutherford B. Hayes High School
Delaware, Ohio

Carolyn E. Waters, J.D., Ed.S.
Georgia Dept. of Education (Ret.)
English Language Arts Consultant
Woodstock, Georgia

Sadlier

Reviewers

The publisher wishes to thank for their comments and suggestions the following teachers and administrators, who read portions of the series prior to publication.

Sr. Maureen Lawrence McDermott, IHM, PhD
Superintendent, Secondary Schools
Archdiocese of Philadelphia Schools
Philadelphia, PA

Aidan T. Brett
Teacher, Language Arts
Springfield High School
Springfield, PA

Kristy L. Raymond
English Teacher, Dept. Chair
Livermore High School
Livermore, CA

Audrey G. Silverman
National Board Certified English Teacher
Dr. Michael Krop Senior High School
Miami, FL

Dawn S. Wolfe
Teacher, English Department
Walnut Hills High School
Cincinnati, OH

Cover: Concept/Art and Design: MK Advertising, Studio Montage and William H. Sadlier, Inc. Cover pencil: Shutterstock.com/VikaSuh.
Photo Credits: age fotostock/Mary Evans Picture Library Ltd/John Cancalosi: 60. akg-images: 76; IAM/World History Archive: 144; National Maritime Museum: 144 *inset*, 145. Alamy Stock Photo/Classic Image: 212 *top*; Corbis Super RF: 124 *inset*; Courtesy: CSU Archives/Everett Collection: 128; Danita Delimont/Claudia Adams: 168; David Levenson: 192; Dmitry Rukhlenko-Travel Photos: 169; Felix Stensson: 88; Judith Collins: 148; Keystone Pictures USA: 101 *right*; North Wind Picture Archives: 216; Pictorial Press Ltd: 101 *left*; Anthony Pierce: 44; Darolyn Quayle: 108; Amoret Tanner: 64; gameover: 13 *bottom*; RGB Ventures/SuperStock: 200; VPC Coins Collection: 176. Art Resource, NY/Digital Image © 2009 Museum Associates/LACMA: 169 *inset*; DeA Picture Library: 168 *inset*; The Art Archive/Society Of The Friends Of Music Vienna/Collection Dagli Orti: 40; Werner Forman: 32; National Portrait Gallery/Smithsonian Institution: 113 *left*; The Metropolitan Museum of Art, New York, NY: 69. Associated Press/Louis Lanzano: 81. Richard Berenholtz: 56–57 *background*. Blend Images/LatinStock Collection: 125. Digital Vision: 124–125. Dorothy Lichtenstein/Private Collection: 68. Dreamstime.com/Rodney Cleasby: 84; Brett Critchley: 152. Georgia Institute of Technology, College of Computing: 201 *bottom*. Getty Images: 100; AFP/Don Emmert: 201 *top*; New York Daily News/Joe Petrella: 189 *left*; Time & Life Pictures: 157 *bottom*; Tom Carter: 220; David Frent: 36, 37 *inset*; George Rinhart: 188; Bettman: 160; Fotosearch/Stringer: 37 *bottom*; Fox Photos/Stringer: 28; H. Armstrong Roberts/ClassicStock: 172; Hulton Archive: 196; Hulton Archive/San Diego Historical Society/Antony Di Gesu: 72; Library of Congress: 37 *top*, 113 *right*; Library of Congress/J.S. Johnson: 24; Photodisc: 113 *inset*, 145 *inset*; Topical Press Agency/Stringer: 120; Universal History Archive: 164. The Granger Collection: 13 *top*. Lebrecht Music, Arts & Authors: 104. Library of Congress, Prints & Photographs Division: 212–213. NASA: 157 *top*. National Portrait Gallery: 213 *top*. New York Public Library Picture Collection: 25 *top*. Newscom/EPA/Michael Reynolds: 112; Reuters/Ali Hashisho: 57; Reuters/Mike Segar: 25 *bottom*; Shen Hong Xinhua News Agency: 056. Science Source: 208. Photodisc: 112 *background*, 112–113. Shutterstock.com/ARENA Creative: 68–69 *background*; argus: 200–201; boumen&japet: 13 *inset*; Daboost: 124; Myotis: 56 *background*, 57; Taiga: 80–81; Thomas Bethge: 188 *inset*; Angelina Dimitrova: 100–101 *background*; Johann Helgason: 37 *top*; Michaela Stejskalova: 12–13; GTS Productions: 132. Superstock/Classicstock.com: 204; Pantheon: 16. US Patent Office: 189 *right*, 189 *right*, 189 *right*. Wikimedia Commons: 20. Ito Yuhan, Cherry Blossoms and Castle: 116. ZUMA Press/Jack Kurtz: 80.

Address inquiries to Permissions Department,
William H. Sadlier, Inc.,
9 Pine Street, New York, New York 10005-4700.

Printed in the United States of America.
ISBN: 978-1-4217-8512-7
4 5 6 7 8 9 10 BRR 24 23 22 21 20

For additional online resources, go to SadlierConnect.com.

CONTENTS

PROGRAM FEATURES ... 6
VOCABULARY IN CONTEXT ... 7
VOCABULARY AND READING ... 8
WORD STUDY ... 10
PRONUNCIATION KEY ... 11

UNIT 1 Across the Pond <Letters> ... 12
Set A: Definitions and Exercises ... 14
Set B: Definitions and Exercises ... 18
Sets A & B: Synonyms; Antonyms; Writing; Vocabulary in Context ... 22

UNIT 2 Constructing the New York City Subway <Historical Nonfiction> ... 24
Set A: Definitions and Exercises ... 26
Set B: Definitions and Exercises ... 30
Sets A & B: Synonyms; Antonyms; Writing; Vocabulary in Context ... 34

UNIT 3 Third Parties in American Politics <Encyclopedia Entry> ... 36
Set A: Definitions and Exercises ... 38
Set B: Definitions and Exercises ... 42
Sets A & B: Synonyms; Antonyms; Writing; Vocabulary in Context ... 46

REVIEW UNITS 1–3
Vocabulary for Comprehension: Part 1 ... 48
Vocabulary for Comprehension: Part 2 ... 50
Synonyms ... 52
Two-Word Completions ... 53

WORD STUDY
Idioms ... 54
Classical Roots ... 55

UNIT 4 Reforming the Security Council <Newspaper Editorial> ... 56
Set A: Definitions and Exercises ... 58
Set B: Definitions and Exercises ... 62
Sets A & B: Synonyms; Antonyms; Writing; Vocabulary in Context ... 66

UNIT 5 What is Pop Art? <Essay> ... 68
Set A: Definitions and Exercises ... 70
Set B: Definitions and Exercises ... 74
Sets A & B: Synonyms; Antonyms; Writing; Vocabulary in Context ... 78

UNIT 6 Your Papers, Please <Debate> ... 80
Set A: Definitions and Exercises ... 82
Set B: Definitions and Exercises ... 86
Sets A & B: Synonyms; Antonyms; Writing; Vocabulary in Context ... 90

REVIEW UNITS 4–6
Vocabulary for Comprehension: Part 1 92
Vocabulary for Comprehension: Part 2 94
Synonyms 96
Two-Word Completions 97

WORD STUDY
Denotation and Connotation 98
Classical Roots 99

UNIT 7 John Lennon's Legacy <Biographical Sketch> 100
Set A: Definitions and Exercises 102
Set B: Definitions and Exercises 106
Sets A & B: Synonyms; Antonyms; Writing; Vocabulary in Context 110

UNIT 8 A Passage to Power <Interview> 112
Set A: Definitions and Exercises 114
Set B: Definitions and Exercise 118
Sets A & B: Synonyms; Antonyms; Writing; Vocabulary in Context 122

UNIT 9 Security Status: It's Complicated <Persuasive Essay> 124
Set A: Definitions and Exercises 126
Set B: Definitions and Exercises 130
Sets A & B: Synonyms; Antonyms; Writing; Vocabulary in Context 134

REVIEW UNITS 7–9
Vocabulary for Comprehension: Part 1 136
Vocabulary for Comprehension: Part 2 138
Synonyms 140
Two-Word Completions 141

WORD STUDY
Idioms 142
Classical Roots 143

UNIT 10 What Happened to the Franklin Expedition? <Magazine Article> 144
Set A: Definitions and Exercises 146
Set B: Definitions and Exercises 150
Sets A & B: Synonyms; Antonyms; Writing; Vocabulary in Context 154

UNIT 11 Apollo 11 Poised for Take-Off <Press Release> 156
Set A: Definitions and Exercises 158
Set B: Definitions and Exercises 162
Sets A & B: Synonyms; Antonyms; Writing; Vocabulary in Context 166

UNIT 12 Pyramids: Monuments to Gods and Men <Compare and Constrast Essay> 168
Set A: Definitions and Exercises 170
Set B: Definitions and Exercises 174
Sets A & B: Synonyms; Antonyms; Writing; Vocabulary in Context 178

REVIEW UNITS 10–12
Vocabulary for Comprehension: Part 1 180
Vocabulary for Comprehension: Part 2 182
Synonyms 184
Two-Word Completions 185

WORD STUDY
Denotation and Connotation 186
Classical Roots 187

UNIT 13 More Than Just a Pretty Face <Profile> 188
Set A: Definitions and Exercises 190
Set B: Definitions and Exercises 194
Sets A & B: Synonyms; Antonyms; Writing; Vocabulary in Context 198

UNIT 14 Artificial Intelligence and Social Robots <Technical Essay> 200
Set A: Definitions and Exercises 202
Set B: Definitions and Exercises 206
Sets A & B: Synonyms; Antonyms; Writing; Vocabulary in Context 210

UNIT 15 Private Life in the Public Eye <Humorous Essay> 212
Set A: Definitions and Exercises 214
Set B: Definitions and Exercises 218
Sets A & B: Synonyms; Antonyms; Writing; Vocabulary in Context 222

REVIEW UNITS 13–15
Vocabulary for Comprehension: Part 1 224
Vocabulary for Comprehension: Part 2 226
Synonyms 228
Two-Word Completions 229

WORD STUDY
Idioms 230
Classical Roots 231

FINAL MASTERY TEST 232

INDEX 239

PROGRAM FEATURES

For more than five decades, **Vocabulary Workshop** has proven to be a highly successful tool for vocabulary growth and the development of vocabulary skills. It has also been shown to help students prepare for standardized tests. **Vocabulary Workshop Achieve** maintains that tradition in a newly designed format.

Each of **Vocabulary Workshop Achieve's** 15 Units introduces 20 words in two 10-word lists—**Set A** and **Set B**. Both Set A and Set B contain exercises to help you develop deeper understanding of the 10 words in each set. Combined Sets A and B then provide practice with all 20 of the words in the Unit. Review and Word Study activities follow Units 3, 6, 9, 12, and 15 and offer practice with the 60 vocabulary words in the preceding three Units.

Each level of **Vocabulary Workshop Achieve** introduces and provides practice with 300 vocabulary words and contains features such as reading passages, writing prompts, vocabulary in context, evidence-based questions, and word study that will help you to master these new vocabulary words and succeed in using skills to comprehend unfamiliar words.

Each Unit in **Vocabulary Workshop Achieve** consists of the following sections for **Set A** and **Set B**: an introductory **Reading Passage** that shows how vocabulary words are used in context, **Definitions** that include sentences that give examples of how to use the words, **Using Context, Choosing the Right Word**, and **Completing the Sentence**—activities that provide practice with the vocabulary words. Each introductory **Reading Passage** is a nonfiction text that includes most of the vocabulary words from the Unit to which it belongs. In addition, **Synonyms**, **Antonyms**, and **Vocabulary in Context** in combined Sets A and B round out each Unit with practice with all 20 Unit words.

The five Review sections cover all 60 words from their corresponding Units. **Vocabulary for Comprehension** is modeled on the reading sections of college entrance exams. It presents reading comprehension questions, including vocabulary-related items and evidence-based items that are based on the reading passages.

Word Study sections that contain activities on **Idioms**, **Denotation and Connotation**, and **Classical Roots** follow the Review. These sections will help you develop your understanding of figurative language and practice skills that will help you to determine the meaning of new and unfamiliar vocabulary.

The Final Mastery Test assesses a selection of words from the year and allows you to see the growth you have made in acquiring new vocabulary words and in mastering the comprehension skills you need to understand unfamiliar words.

ONLINE RESOURCES

SadlierConnect.com

Go to **SadlierConnect.com** to find iWords, an audio program that provides pronunciations, definitions, and examples of usage for all of the vocabulary words presented in this level of **Vocabulary Workshop Achieve**. You can listen to the entire **Reading Passage** and the 20 Unit vocabulary words one word at a time, or download all of the words in any given Unit.

At **SadlierConnect.com** you will also find interactive vocabulary quizzes, flash cards, and interactive games and puzzles that will help reinforce and enrich your understanding of the vocabulary words in this level of **Vocabulary Workshop Achieve**.

VOCABULARY IN CONTEXT

The context of a word is the printed text of which that word is part. By studying a word's context, we may find clues to its meaning. We might find a clue in the immediate or adjoining sentence or phrase in which the word appears; in the topic or subject matter of the passage; or in the physical features—such as photographs, illustrations, charts, graphs, captions, and headings—of a page itself.

The **Reading Passages** as well as the **Using Context**, **Choosing the Right Word**, **Vocabulary in Context**, and **Vocabulary for Comprehension** exercises that appear in the Units, the Reviews, and the Final Mastery Test provide practice in using context to decode and to determine the meaning of unfamiliar words.

Three types of context clues appear in the exercises in this book.

A **restatement clue** consists of a synonym for or a definition of the missing word. For example:

Faithfully reading a weekly newsmagazine not only broadens my knowledge of current events and world or national affairs but also ______________ my vocabulary.

a. decreases **b.** fragments **c.** increases **d.** contains

In this sentence, *broadens* is a synonym of the missing word, *increases*, and acts as a restatement clue for it.

A **contrast clue** consists of an antonym for or a phase that means the opposite of the missing word. For example:

"My view of the situation may be far too rosy," I admitted. "On the other hand, yours may be a bit (**optimistic, bleak**)."

In this sentence, *rosy* is an antonym of the missing word, *bleak*. This is confirmed by the presence of the phrase *on the other hand*, which indicates that the answer must be the opposite of *rosy*.

An **inference clue** implies but does not directly state the meaning of the missing word or words. For example:

"A treat for all ages," the review read, "this wonderful novel combines the ______________ of a scholar with the skill and artistry of an expert ______________ ."

a. ignorance . . . painter **c.** wealth . . . surgeon

b. wisdom . . . beginner **d.** knowledge . . . storyteller

In this sentence, there are several inference clues: (a) the word *scholar* suggests knowledge; (b) the words *novel*, *artistry*, and *skill* suggest the word *storyteller*. These words are inference clues because they suggest or imply, but do not directly state, the missing word or words.

VOCABULARY AND READING

There is a strong connection between vocabulary knowledge and reading comprehension. Although comprehension is much more than recognizing words and knowing their meanings, comprehension is nearly impossible if you do not know an adequate number of words in the text you are reading or have the vocabulary skills to figure out their meaning.

The **Reading Passages** in this level provide extra practice with vocabulary words. Vocabulary words are in boldface to draw your attention to their uses and contexts. Context clues embedded in the passages encourage you to figure out the meanings of words before you read the definitions provided on the pages directly following the passages.

Test Prep

Your knowledge of word meanings and your ability to think carefully about what you read will help you succeed in school and on standardized tests, including the SAT® and ACT® exams.

The **Vocabulary for Comprehension** exercises in each Review consist of a reading passage followed by comprehension questions. The passages and questions are similar to those that you are likely to find on standardized tests.

Types of Questions

You are likely to encounter the following types of questions in **Vocabulary Workshop Achieve** and on standardized tests.

Main Idea Questions generally ask what the passage as a whole is about. Often, but not always, the main idea is stated in the first paragraph of the passage. You may also be asked the main idea of a specific paragraph. Questions about the main idea may begin like this:

- The primary or main purpose of the passage is . . .
- The author's primary or main purpose in the passage is to . . .
- Which of the following statements most nearly paraphrases the author's main idea in the ninth paragraph (lines 77–88)?
- The main purpose of the fourth paragraph (lines 16–45) is to . . .

Detail Questions focus on important information that is explicitly stated in the passage. Often, however, the correct answer choices do not use the exact language of the passage. They are instead restatements, or paraphrases, of the text.

Vocabulary in Context Questions check your ability to use context to identify a word's meaning. For example:

- As it is used in paragraph 2, "adherents" most nearly means . . .

Use the word's context in a passage to select the best answer, particularly when the vocabulary word has more than one meaning. The answer choices may contain two (or more) correct meanings of the word in question. Choose the meaning that best fits the context.

Inference Questions ask you to make inferences or draw conclusions from the passage. These questions often begin like this:

- It can be most reasonably inferred from the information in the fifth paragraph (lines 53–69) that . . .
- The passage clearly implies that . . .

The inferences you make and the conclusions you draw must be based on the information in the passage. Using the facts you learn from the passage in addition to the knowledge and reasoning you already have helps you understand what is implied and reach conclusions that are logical.

Evidence-Based Questions ask you to provide evidence from the passage that will support the answer you provided to a previous question. These questions often begin like this:

- Which choice provides the best evidence for the answer to the previous question?
- Which statement is the best evidence for the answer to the previous question?

Questions About Tone show your understanding of the author's attitude toward the topic of the passage. To determine the tone, pay attention to the author's word choice. The author's attitude may be positive (respectful), negative (scornful), or neutral (distant). These are typical questions:

- The author's primary purpose in the passage is to . . .
- Which word best describes the author's tone?

Questions About Author's Technique focus on the way a text is organized and the language the author uses. These questions ask you to think about structure and function. For example:

- In the context of the passage, the primary function of the fourth paragraph (lines 30–37) is to . . .
- The organizational structure of the passage is best described as . . .

To answer the questions, you must demonstrate an understanding of the way the author presents information and develops ideas.

VOCABULARY AND WRITING

The **Writing: Words in Action** prompt provides you with an opportunity to practice using text evidence to respond to a prompt about the introductory **Reading Passage**. You will have the opportunity to demonstrate your understanding of the Unit words by incorporating the new vocabulary you have learned into your own writing.

WORD STUDY

Word Study helps build word knowledge with strategies to help you look closely at words for meanings. Word Study instruction and practice include **Idioms**, **Denotation and Connotation**, and **Classical Roots**.

Idioms

Three Word Study sections feature instruction on and practice with idioms. An idiom is an informal expression whose literal meaning does not help the reader or listener understand what the expression means, such as "raining cats and dogs," "the apple of my eye," or "a dark horse." While every language has its own idioms, English is particularly rich in idioms and idiomatic expressions. Developing a clear understanding of idioms will help you better understand the figurative language that authors use in their writing.

Denotation and Connotation

Instruction in **Denotation and Connotation** and practice with connotations is included in two of the Word Study sections. Understanding a word's connotation will develop your skills as a reader, writer, and speaker.

Understanding the difference between denotation and connotation is important to understanding definitions and how concepts are used, as well as in choosing the right word. In these exercises, practice choosing the correct word by determining the emotional association of the word.

Classical Roots

Each Word Study includes a **Classical Roots** exercise that provides instruction in and practice with Greek and Latin roots. Developing a useful, transferable technique to make sense out of unfamiliar words through Greek and Latin roots will help you unlock the meanings of thousands of words. An example word drawn from the vocabulary words in the previous Units is referenced at the top of the page and serves as a guide to help you complete the exercise.

PRONUNCIATION KEY

The pronunciation is indicated for every basic word in this book. The pronunciation symbols used are similar to those used in most recent standard dictionaries. The author has primarily consulted *Webster's Third New International Dictionary* and *The Random House Dictionary of the English Language* (*Unabridged*). Many English words have multiple accepted pronunciations. The author has given one pronunciation when such words occur in this book except when the pronunciation changes according to the part of speech. For example, the verb *project* is pronounced **prə jekt′**, and the noun form is pronounced **präj′ ekt**.

Vowels	ā	lake	e	stress	ü	loot, new
	a	mat	ī	knife	u̇	foot, pull
	â	care	i	sit	ə	jump, broken
	ä	bark, bottle	ō	flow	ər	bird, better
	au̇	doubt	ô	all, cord		
	ē	beat, wordy	oi	oil		

Consonants	ch	child, lecture	s	cellar	wh	what
	g	give	sh	shun	y	yearn
	j	gentle, bridge	th	thank	z	is
	ŋ	sing	t̶h̶	those	zh	measure

All other consonants are sounded as in the alphabet.

Stress The accent mark follows the syllable receiving the major stress: en rich′.

Abbreviations	*adj.*	adjective	*n.*	noun	*prep.*	preposition
	adv.	adverb	*part.*	participle	*v.*	verb
	int.	interjection	*pl.*	plural		

*Read the following passage, taking note of the **boldface** words and their contexts. These words are among those you will be studying in Unit 1. It may help you to complete the exercises in this Unit if you refer to the way the words are used below.*

Across the Pond

<Letters>

January 27, 1891

My Dear Cora,

Accept my congratulations on the establishment of the National American Women's Suffrage Association. Am I too bold to presume this new unity in the American suffrage movement marks the end of the **invidious** divisions in your ranks? English appetite for American news is **insatiable** of late, with much talk of means by which we might **emulate** your recent achievements. Just yesterday, at a small gathering of friends of our League, I heard Mrs. Pankhurst break off into a rousing **encomium** on the entry of the state of Wyoming into your union. The opinion here is that with one state now granting universal suffrage, it's only a matter of time before the dam breaks.

In England we persuade ourselves to **eschew** hope for such grand achievements till the times make them more **tenable**. There's plenty of work to be done to prepare for the event. The Pankhursts have inspired many of us to push for the women's vote in local elections. This would be no small thing in itself, and should help our effort to reform the conservative spirit of our country. I fear the climate in America is more favorable to the endeavor, while opposition here remains **intransigent**. At tea not long ago, I heard one Mr. Evans produce the most **banal** argument against the women's vote you could imagine. I won't trouble you with details of his **carping** rhetoric, but note that he took pains to demonstrate that women are "unfit for the public duties of citizenship," and greatly feared the prospect that women's votes might "swamp the votes of men." Imagine my delight when, pressed by objections from several present, the good Mr. Evans grew suddenly **taciturn**, and at a loss for any other means of **temporizing**, complimented his hostess and bid us good day!

Charles and I often recall your kindness during our last visit, and look forward to seeing you again this summer.

Affectionately,

Millicent

March 20, 1891

Dearest Millie,

We have many like your Mr. Evans here, which puts our own work ahead of us. I can, however, **substantiate** your optimism where Wyoming is concerned. Other Western states and territories will surely follow suit, with energy already in the project in Idaho, Colorado, and elsewhere. Women's suffrage has firmer roots in the West, and we expect more progress there.

Germane to the topic, I had the privilege of meeting Jane Addams in Chicago, where she has founded the Hull House, devoted to the education of local women of the working class. Miss Addams is a remarkable woman, and strikes me as the very type to carry our movement forward. Initial renovations of the Hull Mansion were funded primarily through her own **largesse**, and she has become an advocate for local suffrage in Chicago and for other progressive causes.

Our new Association might show the extent to which the old arguments that divided us have passed into history, but new excuses for dissent emerge as old ones fade. The new tendency to portray women as "domestic" spirits, superior in moral virtue to men, strikes some of us as misguided. I'll not **belabor** the point here, hoping instead to present a **coherent** argument for you in person when you arrive in New York.

Until then, I keep you in my thoughts. Your friend always,

Cora

Audio

For iWords and audio passages, go to **SadlierConnect.com**.

Jane Addams
"The Suffragette," June 13, 1913.
Registered at the G.P.O. as a Newspaper
The Suffragette
The Official Organ of the Women's Social and Political Union
Price 1d. Weekly
Edited by Christabel Pankhurst.
FRIDAY, JUNE 13, 1913.
No. 35—Vol. 1.

American women fought for the right to vote in each state, until the Nineteenth Amendment was passed in 1920.

Definitions

Note the spelling, pronunciation, part(s) of speech, and definition(s) of each of the following words. Then write the appropriate form of the word in the blank space in the illustrative sentence(s) following.

1. arrogate
(a′ rə gāt)
(*v.*) to claim or take without right
The ambitious noblemen will put the young king under house arrest and ______________ royal privileges to themselves.

2. banal
(bə nal′)
(*adj.*) hackneyed, trite, commonplace
The new play's ______________ dialogue made it seem more like a soap opera than a serious drama.

3. coherent
(kō hēr′ ənt)
(*adj.*) holding or sticking together; making a logical whole; comprehensible, meaningful
The physics teacher gave a surprisingly ______________ description of quantum mechanics.

4. emulate
(em′ yə lāt)
(*v.*) to imitate with the intent of equaling or surpassing the model
Most beginning writers try to ______________ a great writer and later develop their own individual styles.

5. encomium
(en kō′ mē əm)
(*n.*) a formal expression of praise, a lavish tribute
On Veterans Day, the President delivered a heartfelt ______________ to those who died for their country.

6. germane
(jər mān′)
(*adj.*) relevant, appropriate, apropos, fitting
Bringing up examples from the past is not ______________ to the present discussion.

7. intransigent
(in tran′ sə jənt)
(*adj.*) refusing to compromise, irreconcilable
Little will get accomplished if the legislators of both parties maintain their ______________ attitudes.

8. reconnaissance
(ri kän′ ə səns)
(*n.*) a survey made for military purposes; any kind of preliminary inspection or examination
The field officer required a thorough ______________ before ordering any troop movements.

9. substantiate (səb stan′ shē āt)
(*v.*) to establish by evidence, prove; to give concrete or substantial form to

The prospector was unable to ____________ his claim to the land where the gold was found.

10. temporize (tem′ pə rīz)
(*v.*) to stall or act evasively in order to gain time, avoid a confrontation, or postpone a decision; to compromise

For most of Shakespeare's great tragedy, the protagonist Hamlet chooses to ____________ rather than act.

Using Context

For each item, determine whether the ***boldface*** *word from pages 14–15 makes sense in the context of the sentence. Circle the item numbers next to the six sentences in which the words are used correctly.*

1. The mechanic will carefully inspect the engine and replace any parts that are damaged or **germane**.

2. In her opening address to the jury, the prosecutor promised that she would present solid evidence to **substantiate** the charges against the defendant.

3. If you want to be a good debater, you must be able to form and deliver a brief but **coherent** message with very little preparation time.

4. I would definitely recommend this surprisingly **banal** book by a first-time author to anyone who is looking for an exciting and entertaining reading experience.

5. Despite many hours of **reconnaissance**, no trace of the missing plane was ever found.

6. The agreement, which was meant to ensure fairness, stated that neither country would **arrogate** the other's fishing rights in the rich offshore waters.

7. He was an agreeable person, always willing to approach any difference of opinion with an **intransigent** point of view.

8. The essay, an **encomium** to a beloved friend whom the writer had known since childhood, brought tears to our eyes.

9. If you don't **temporize** your passport in the next six months, it will expire.

10. In my opinion, it would be impossible for any poet, no matter how gifted, to **emulate** the startling freshness of Emily Dickinson's language and imagery.

Choosing the Right Word

*Select the **boldface** word that better completes each sentence. You might refer to the passage on pages 12–13 to see how most of these words are used in context. Note that the choices might be related forms of the Unit words.*

1. Ethelred the Unready was so reluctant to face the Vikings who invaded his kingdom that in effect he (**arrogated, temporized**) himself off the throne.

2. The historian needed to scrutinize additional handwriting samples before he could (**emulate, substantiate**) the signature on the document.

3. The speech was so filled with (**encomiums, reconnaissance**) that I found it hard to believe that the subject of all this acclaim was plain old me.

4. The poor woman was in such a state of shock after the accident that she couldn't give a(n) (**coherent, intransigent**) account of what had happened.

5. The Constitution is uniquely designed to provide protection against those who might seek to (**substantiate, arrogate**) undue power to themselves.

6. I am proud to have it said of me that I am stubborn and (**germane, intransigent**) when genuine moral issues are involved.

7. Even a very imperfect human being may sometimes have virtues of mind or character that are worthy of (**reconnaissance, emulation**).

8. Your critical comments about my "lack of social background" may be true, but they are not (**coherent, germane**) to my qualifications for office.

9. What evidence can you offer to (**substantiate, temporize**) the assertion that capital punishment does not deter potential murderers?

10. In that moment of grief, the conventional expressions of sympathy I had always considered (**coherent, banal**) were surprisingly comforting.

11. Aerial (**reconnaissance, encomium**) of the enemy's positions provided the general with the information he needed to plan his attack.

12. In her first acting role, she tried to (**emulate, substantiate**) an Oscar-winning actress but instead the critics thought she deserved the Golden Raspberry award.

Completing the Sentence

Choose the word from the word bank that best completes each of the following sentences. Write the correct word or form of the word in the space provided.

arrogate	**coherent**	**encomium**	**intransigent**	**substantiate**
banal	**emulate**	**germane**	**reconnaissance**	**temporize**

1. The purpose of military ____________________ remains the same whether cavalry or helicopters are used: to learn as much as possible about the enemy.

2. There is nothing wrong with ____________________ the great singers of the past as long as you eventually develop a style that is all your own.

3. How can we "meet them halfway" when they are so ____________________ in their opposition to what we propose to do?

4. In any crisis, the longer a person ____________________, the greater the danger is likely to become.

5. By whose authority did you ____________________ to yourself the right to decide how the club's money would be spent?

6. Even the most severe critics showered ____________________ on the young writer for the remarkable narrative power of her first novel.

7. Some of the episodes in the series were wonderfully fresh and original; others were just plain ____________________.

8. I doubt very much that he can ____________________ his assertion that he won two gold medals in the 1956 Olympics.

9. Your essay would be a great deal tighter and more ____________________ if you removed all the extraneous information it now contains.

10. I don't object to the inclusion of anecdotes in a serious lecture, but they should at the very least be ____________________ to the subject.

End Set A

Definitions

Note the spelling, pronunciation, part(s) of speech, and definition(s) of each of the following words. Then write the appropriate form of the word in the blank space in the illustrative sentence(s) following.

1. acquisitive (ə kwiz′ ə tiv)
(*adj.*) able to get and retain ideas or information; concerned with acquiring wealth or property
In an ____________________ society, there is a great deal of emphasis on buying and selling.

2. belabor (bi lā′ bər)
(*v.*) to work on excessively; to thrash soundly
His tendency to ____________________ the small points often made him miss the big picture.

3. carping (kär′ piŋ)
(*adj.*) tending to find fault, especially in a petty, nasty, or hairsplitting way; (*n.*) petty, nagging criticism
The trainee resigned after a week rather than put up with the ____________________ complaints of the sales manager.
Most artists choose to ignore the ____________________ of critics and simply go on with their work.

4. congeal (kən jēl′)
(*v.*) to change from liquid to solid, thicken; to make inflexible or rigid
If you do not wash your dishes right away, the food on them will ____________________.

5. eschew (es chü′)
(*v.*) to avoid, shun, keep away from
The young athletes promised the coach that they would train vigorously and ____________________ bad habits.

6. insatiable (in sā′ shə bəl)
(*adj.*) so great or demanding as not to be satisfied
People with an ____________________ appetite for gossip often do not have compelling stories of their own.

7. invidious (in vid′ ē əs)
(*adj.*) offensive, hateful; tending to cause bitterness and resentment
Bosses should avoid making ____________________ comparisons between their employees.

8. largesse (lär jes′)
(*n.*) generosity in giving; lavish or bountiful contributions
The university was the fortunate beneficiary of the ____________________ of many of its graduates.

9. taciturn (tas′ ə tərn)
(*adj.*) habitually silent or quiet, inclined to talk very little
Woodrow Wilson has the reputation of having a dour and ____________ personality.

10. tenable (ten′ ə bəl)
(*adj.*) capable of being held or defended
The researchers put forth a ____________ theory, but their conclusions would be reviewed carefully by others.

Using Context

*For each item, determine whether the **boldface** word from pages 18–19 makes sense in the context of the sentence. Circle the item numbers next to the six sentences in which the words are used correctly.*

1. The king's **insatiable** need for power drove him to dispatch his subjects on countless invasions of neighboring territories.
2. We were all impressed by the **largesse** she displayed when standing up to the bully, and we all vowed to mirror her bravery in the future.
3. To win the debate, we must not only be able to defend our own arguments, but also prove that the opposing side's statements are not **tenable**.
4. She is known to be particularly **taciturn**, but when she does speak, she always has something valuable to say.
5. The editor cautioned the author to not **belabor** his own viewpoints in the novel so much that he forgot to tell the story.
6. You can tell that he was once a reporter by his **invidious** nature, as he always wants to know everything about everyone.
7. Relationships between acquaintances sometimes **congeal**, resulting in the breakdown of the friendship.
8. Her mind is so **acquisitive** that it often seems that whatever I say goes in one ear and out the other.
9. The couple rarely fight about big issues, but instead they both constantly make **carping** comments to one another about the silliest things.
10. I vowed to **eschew** all unhealthy food as soon as I began my diet, but within an hour was tempted by cupcakes brought out for someone's birthday.

Choosing the Right Word

*Select the **boldface** word that better completes each sentence. You might refer to the passage on pages 12–13 to see how most of these words are used in context. Note that the choices might be related forms of the Unit words.*

1. Famous for his monosyllabic replies to questions and a somber and (**taciturn, acquisitive**) nature, President Coolidge had the nickname "Silent Cal."

2. After the editor read the story, she returned it to the author with only a few (**carping, invidious**) criticisms of minor faults penciled in the margin.

3. In our attempt to improve the quality of life in America, we should not be too quick to (**eschew, belabor**) old ideas simply because they are old.

4. The new batting champion in our softball league is a(n) (**insatiable, taciturn**) young man who prefers to let his bat do his talking for him.

5. Aristotle had such a(n) (**tenable, acquisitive**) mind that his writings are a veritable gold mine of odd and interesting information.

6. The mood of cordiality with which we began the meeting soon (**congealed, eschewed**) into icy politeness.

7. "That word has such (**invidious, taciturn**) connotations in modern American parlance," I said, "that I would hesitate to use it, even in jest."

8. The (**carping, largesse**) of grateful patients made the clinic's expansion possible.

9. His figure bears witness to his (**tenable, insatiable**) appetite for the pleasures of the table.

10. Because this committee has (**belabored, eschewed**) the issue of zoning laws for months, we will not invite public comments on it again in tonight's meeting.

11. When the evidence of her misconduct became irrefutable, she saw that her position was not (**carping, tenable**) and resigned.

12. Suddenly a band of ruffians set upon us and began to (**congeal, belabor**) us with blows and curses.

Completing the Sentence

Choose the word from the word bank that best completes each of the following sentences. Write the correct word or form of the word in the space provided.

acquisitive	**carping**	**eschew**	**invidious**	**taciturn**
belabor	**congeal**	**insatiable**	**largesse**	**tenable**

1. Students who seek high grades must learn to ____________________ the joys of that one-eyed monster, the television.

2. In spite of his size, he was so ____________________ that we tended to forget that he was even in the room.

3. Never having any money in one's pockets can be a real trial for someone born with the ____________________ instincts of a pack rat.

4. She received housing vouchers and food stamps as a result of the government's ____________________.

5. The novel contains an interesting study of a miser's ____________________ lust for gold and its evil effects on those around him.

6. Despite the ____________________ and nit-picking of a few petty minds, I feel we have substantially improved our local school system of late.

7. "There is no need for you to ____________________ the point," I replied, "when I already understand clearly what your criticism is."

8. When the temperature outside dropped suddenly, the muddy water in the ditch ____________________ into a mass of icy sludge.

9. In my opinion, there is absolutely no justification for making such ____________________ distinctions between the two types of product.

10. As a result of recent research, earlier theories about the origin of the universe are no longer ____________________.

End Set B

Synonyms

*Choose the word or form of the word from this Unit that is the same or most nearly the same in meaning as the **boldface** word or expression in the phrase. Write that word on the line. Use a dictionary if necessary.*

1. led the **scouting expedition** into the jungle ________________
2. the **grasping** real estate developer ________________
3. **mimic** her mannerisms ________________
4. blood that does not **coagulate** ________________
5. tends to **hedge** when confronted by direct questions ________________
6. **uncompromising** about changing the curfew ________________
7. **pertinent** to the case ________________
8. tried to **usurp** control of the finances ________________
9. could not **verify** the alibi ________________
10. **nit-picking** over tiny details ________________
11. the puppy's **voracious** hunger ________________
12. **harp on** the same point again and again ________________
13. was thanked for her **munificence** ________________
14. received a well-deserved **commendation** ________________
15. the **defensible** castle wall ________________

Antonyms

*Choose the word or form of the word from this Unit that is most nearly opposite in meaning to the **boldface** word or expression in the phrase. Write that word on the line. Use a dictionary if necessary.*

1. appeared **garrulous** in public ________________
2. the **inspired** lyrics to that song ________________
3. **embrace** drinking caffeine before bed ________________
4. made a **disjointed** argument ________________
5. made a very **magnanimous** remark ________________

Writing: Words in Action

Suppose you are Cora's friend and a fellow member of the National American Women's Suffrage Association. Write an essay persuading men in the Western states that women should have the right to vote. Use at least two details from the passage (pages 12–13) and three or more words from the Unit.

Vocabulary in Context

*Some of the words you have studied in this Unit appear in **boldface** type. Read the passage below, and then circle the letter of the correct answer for each word as it is used in context.*

George Bernard Shaw is reputed to have remarked that the British and the Americans were "two peoples divided by a common language." There's no concrete evidence that he did say it, but it's the kind of thing he said all the time.

The differences in British and American English originated with the Pilgrims who emigrated to America in the 1600s. There's no doubting their courage or resolve, but they were woefully underprepared to start a new life in the "new world." Among their numbers were no working farmers, and the hold of the *Mayflower* was not packed with plows, fishing lines and nets, or animal traps—perhaps they thought such things would be **invidious** in the new Eden. They began to **arrogate** to themselves the power to name America's flora and fauna, and in doing so revealed an astonishing unfamiliarity with nature. When confronted with an unfamiliar species, they gave it the name of an unrelated species from England. So that big fat bird with the red breast and the cheerful song became a robin even though it is a completely different species and genus than the European robin. They misnamed blackbirds, swallows, larks, and hedgehogs, and saw beech trees, walnut trees, laurel, bay, and hemlock where there were none. Confronted with something completely unknown, Pilgrims would put old words together in a new way and let them **congeal**: copperhead, eggplant, rattlesnake.

Pilgrims were not **acquisitive** of new words in their **reconnaissance** of the New World, but they were so **intransigent** about sticking to the old ones that the words long outlived their originals in the Old World: *fall* has long been displaced by *autumn* in England. A "deck" of cards became a pack of cards in England some time ago.

---

1. To be **invidious** is to be
a. helpful **c.** necessary
b. undesirable **d.** thoughtless

2. The word **arrogate** most nearly means
a. deny **c.** take
b. hoard **d.** strike

3. If things **congeal**, they
a. stick **c.** solidify
b. explode **d.** dissolve

4. An **acquisitive** person
a. enjoys novelty **c.** is afraid
b. collects things **d.** is stubborn

5. A **reconnaissance** is
a. a rediscovery **c.** an adventure
b. a test of recall **d.** an exploration

6. An **intransigent** person acts
a. without compromise **c.** with bad intent
b. impulsively **d.** blindly

Read the following passage, taking note of the ***boldface*** *words and their contexts. These words are among those you will be studying in Unit 2. It may help you to complete the exercises in this Unit if you refer to the way the words are used below.*

Constructing the New York City Subway

<Historical Nonfiction>

By 1900, nearly four million people lived in New York City, about five times as many as had lived in the same area fifty years earlier. The **celerity** of the population's increase was driven by a range of factors including economic growth, industrialization, and immigration. As an **overt** symptom of the prosperity of the city and the nation, rapid population growth was welcomed by many of the city's inhabitants. But the increase in population posed serious challenges. **Myopic** disregard for the supply of housing left many of the city's poorer inhabitants crammed into crowded tenements until construction began to keep pace. And the growing mass of people traveling throughout the city created unprecedented amounts of traffic in the streets.

Traffic congestion swelled beyond the bounds of **propriety**. Traffic accidents were all too common, as drivers of horse-drawn omnibuses, in a rush to pick up passengers and earn fares, saw fit to trample pedestrians along the way. Street traffic was a constant target of **animadversion** in the press. But it was also a cause of innovation. As the streams of pedestrians and horse-drawn carriages grew steadily through the nineteenth century, railroads were elevated above street level to avoid interference with the **maelstrom** of traffic on the streets. Steam-powered elevated railways were soon replaced by cleaner electric-powered elevated lines.

Plans for building a subway had been drawn as early as the 1860s, but the project was stalled for decades by **devious** local politics. Operators of surface railways and horse-drawn cars, who feared competition from the subway, cast the plan in a **pejorative** light, claiming it was impractical and bound to fail. The **suppliant**

Elevated trains on Manhattan's Bowery, 1895

Left: Subway construction, 1902; Below: Vintage NYC subway, 2004

protests of property owners who worried that prolonged subway construction would interfere with business helped strengthen opposition to the subway. **Avid** supporters of the subway plan, on the other hand, considered any opposition to be **sacrilege**. But adversity will not last forever. In the end, the clear benefits that the subway would bring to the city by increasing the speed of transit and by alleviating the traffic on the streets proved more compelling than the political **gambits** employed by opponents. After decades of false starts, **incendiary** rhetoric, and **histrionic** arguments on both sides, a contract for construction was signed on February 21, 1900. Construction began **summarily** in the following months.

Thousands of laborers worked on the project. Most of the tunnels were built using the "cut-and-cover" method: Workers dug trenches through the streets and covered them with wooden planks and bridges to allow traffic to pass overhead while work continued. Down in the trenches, workers laid the tracks, built the subway stations, and surrounded the subway with steel and concrete. Then they rebuilt the street above. The construction company that built the subway was also responsible for building the coal-fueled generators that would produce the subway's electricity.

The subway opened to the public on October 27, 1904. About 150,000 people stood in line to pay the five-cent fare for a rocky, **undulating** ride on what was then the fastest public transportation system in the world. Over the next few decades, the city's subway system was expanded and integrated with the elevated lines above ground. An impressive feat of engineering for its time, the New York City subway system remains one of the largest in the world to this day.

Audio

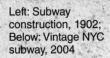

For iWords and audio passages, go to **SadlierConnect.com**.

Definitions

Note the spelling, pronunciation, part(s) of speech, and definition(s) of each of the following words. Then write the appropriate form of the word in the blank space in the illustrative sentence(s) following.

1. accost (ə käst′)
(*v.*) to approach and speak to first; to confront in a challenging or aggressive way
The nobleman was ________________ by beggars on his way to the castle.

2. brackish (brak′ ish)
(*adj.*) having a salty taste and unpleasant to drink
The shipwrecked passengers adrift on the lifeboat became ill after drinking ________________ water.

3. celerity (sə ler′ ə tē)
(*n.*) swiftness, rapidity of motion or action
Heavy snowfall was expected, so the highway department responded with surprising ________________.

4. halcyon (hal′ sē ən)
(*n.*) a legendary bird identified with the kingfisher; (*adj.*) of or relating to the halcyon; calm, peaceful; happy, golden; prosperous, affluent
The teacher read the legend of the ________________, a mythic bird that nested in a calm sea.
The woman often spoke of the ________________ days of her childhood.

5. incendiary (in sen′ dē er ē)
(*adj.*) deliberately setting or causing fires; designed to start fires; tending to stir up strife or rebellion; (*n.*) one who deliberately sets fires, arsonist; one who causes strife
The arsonist planted an ________________ device in the basement of the store.
The radical ________________ was sentenced to life imprisonment.

6. maelstrom (māl′ strəm)
(*n.*) a whirlpool of great size and violence; a situation resembling a whirlpool in violence and destruction
Many innocent people caught in the ________________ of the revolution lost their lives and property.

7. overt (ō vert′)
(*adj.*) open, not hidden, expressed or revealed in a way that is easily recognized
In order for Congress to declare war, the President must demonstrate an ________________ threat.

8. pejorative (pə jôr′ ə tiv)
(*adj.*) tending to make worse; expressing disapproval or disparagement, derogatory, deprecatory, belittling
The lawyer was accused of making a ________________ remark when referring to the defendant's background.

9. suppliant (səp′ lē ənt)

(*adj.*) asking humbly and earnestly; (*n.*) one who makes a request humbly and earnestly, a petitioner, suitor

He made a ____________________ plea to the parole board.

Stranded in Moscow, Napoleon had to turn to the czar not as a conqueror but as a ____________________.

10. undulate (ən′ dyə lāt)

(*v.*) to move in waves or with a wavelike motion; to have a wavelike appearance or form

The baseball fans began to ____________________ as they cheered, so that they appeared to move in a wave.

Using Context

*For each item, determine whether the **boldface** word from pages 26–27 makes sense in the context of the sentence. Circle the item numbers next to the six sentences in which the words are used correctly.*

1. The patch of tall grass will gently **undulate** every time a breeze passes through it.
2. In the legend of Atlantis, the city enjoyed many **halcyon** years before the citizens became corrupt and greedy and the gods decided to bring destruction upon them.
3. When mixed with water, salt acts as a **suppliant**, lowering the temperature for freezing.
4. The **celerity** of the country was a welcome reprieve from the hustle and bustle of the city.
5. The movie's high-tech special effects depicted the **maelstrom** that resulted from Earth's collision with a large asteroid.
6. These wool-lined hiking boots will **accost** your feet and keep them warm and dry.
7. The **incendiary** efforts to reintroduce the species to its native habitat have been successful.
8. Despite showing no **overt** signs of illness, the patient reported feeling extremely weak and ill.
9. The phrase *needs improvement* is mildly critical, while the phrase *ridiculously inadequate* is harshly **pejorative**.
10. We paddled for days, starting in crystal clear water at the river's source and ending in **brackish** water where the river emptied into the sea.

Choosing the Right Word

*Select the **boldface** word that better completes each sentence. You might refer to the passage on pages 24–25 to see how most of these words are used in context. Note that the choices might be related forms of the Unit words.*

1. John Masefield's poem "Sea Fever" has a(n) (**halcyon, undulating**) rhythm that actually gives one the feeling of being on a rolling ship.

2. As reported in several online news sites, the (**incendiary, halcyon**) accused in the destructive forest fires has admitted his guilt.

3. Instead of imbibing the (**brackish, suppliant**) waters of superstition, let us refresh ourselves with long drafts of pure, clean common sense.

4. As the defendant left the courtroom, he was (**undulated, accosted**) by a group of reporters seeking his reaction to the verdict.

5. "His acts of defiance have been so (**brackish, overt**) and premeditated that I have no choice but to fire him," she said sadly.

6. Walt tends to react slowly, but when he feels that his own interests are at stake he can move with striking (**celerity, maelstrom**).

7. His reckless words had an (**incendiary, overt**) effect on the already excited crowd, and large-scale rioting resulted.

8. The infatuated schoolboy, in one of his more restrained expressions, described himself as "a (**celerity, suppliant**) at the altar of love."

9. Because the word *appeasement* is associated with disastrous concessions to Adolf Hitler, it has acquired a(n) (**pejorative, overt**) connotation.

10. Nary a ripple disturbed the (**halcyon, brackish**) calm of the sea on that glorious summer's afternoon.

11. She was buffeted about in a veritable (**incendiary, maelstrom**) of emotions, caused mainly by her own dissatisfaction with herself.

12. My (**pejorative, suppliant**) request for a later curfew proved successful.

Completing the Sentence

Choose the word from the word bank that best completes each of the following sentences. Write the correct word or form of the word in the space provided.

accost	**celerity**	**incendiary**	**overt**	**suppliant**
brackish	**halcyon**	**maelstrom**	**pejorative**	**undulate**

1. The tons of ____________________ material ignited and turned the waste disposal plant into a roaring inferno.

2. I stand before you an abject ____________________, hoping against hope for a sign of your forgiveness.

3. The Japanese attack on Pearl Harbor was a(n) ____________________ act of war.

4. The suffix *-ling* often has a(n) ____________________ connotation, as in the word *princeling*, derived from *prince*.

5. Many a rich Southern planter saw all his financial resources swallowed up in the ____________________ of the Civil War.

6. The ____________________ with which he accepted our invitation to dinner suggested that he was badly in need of a good meal.

7. During the rainy season, the highway sank at so many points that its surface began to ____________________ like the track for a roller coaster.

8. We looked back on those ____________________ years before the war broke out as a kind of "golden age" in our history.

9. As an employee of the local polling service last summer, I had to ____________________ people on the street and ask their opinions.

10. To our dismay, we discovered that the water we had worked so hard to bring to the surface was too ____________________ for human consumption.

End Set A

Definitions

Note the spelling, pronunciation, part(s) of speech, and definition(s) of each of the following words. Then write the appropriate form of the word in the blank space in the illustrative sentence(s) following.

1. animadversion (an ə mad vər′ zhən)
(*n.*) a comment indicating strong criticism or disapproval
The inexperienced filmmaker was disheartened by the ____________________ of the film critic.

2. avid (av′ id)
(*adj.*) desirous of something to the point of greed; intensely eager
Most writers are also ____________________ readers who have loved books since childhood.

3. devious (dē′ vē əs)
(*adj.*) straying or wandering from a straight or direct course; done or acting in a shifty or underhanded way
The interrogator used ____________________ methods to try to get the suspect to incriminate himself.

4. gambit (gam′ bit)
(*n.*) in chess, an opening move that involves risk or sacrifice of a minor piece in order to gain a later advantage; any opening move of this type
Asking an interesting stranger about his or her job is a popular party ____________________.

5. histrionic (his trē än′ ik)
(*adj.*) pertaining to actors and their techniques; theatrical, artificial; melodramatic
Upon receiving his award, the young actor gave a ____________________ speech.

6. myopic (mī äp′ ik)
(*adj.*) nearsighted; lacking a broad, realistic view of a situation; lacking foresight or discernment
The ____________________ foreign policy of the last administration has led to serious problems with our allies.

7. propriety (prə prī′ ə tē)
(*n.*) the state of being proper, appropriateness; (*pl.*) standards of what is proper or socially acceptable
The social worker questioned the ____________________ of the police's request to see confidential records.

8. sacrilege (sak′ rə lij)
(*n.*) improper or disrespectful treatment of something held sacred
The anthropologist was accused of committing a ____________________ when she disturbed a burial ground.

9. summarily (sə mer′ ə lē) — (*adv.*) without delay or formality; briefly, concisely

As soon as there was evidence of criminal wrongdoing, the official was ____________ ousted from his post.

10. talisman (tal′ iz mən) — (*n.*) an object that serves as a charm or is believed to confer magical powers, an amulet, fetish

Most people do not believe that rabbit's feet and other ____________ actually bring good luck.

Using Context

*For each item, determine whether the **boldface** word from pages 30–31 makes sense in the context of the sentence. Circle the item numbers next to the six sentences in which the words are used correctly.*

1. The contestant refused to resort to **devious** methods to win the game despite the cheating of the other players.
2. When she saw her favorite actor on the street, her sense of **propriety** went out the window, and she ran up to the celebrity and started peppering him with questions.
3. A bad experience with a dog in childhood may lead a person to have an **animadversion** to dogs as an adult.
4. The manager was skilled at anticipating potential problems with a project and planning a **myopic** strategy for dealing with them.
5. Although I repeatedly told him that we needed to hurry in order to catch the train, he walked **summarily** down the street as if he hadn't a care in the world.
6. As an **avid** viewer of reality television, she seems to know more about the lives of strangers than about her own friends and family.
7. His reaction to the news was so **histrionic** that I imagine he was trying to garner sympathy rather than expressing genuine sorrow.
8. Whenever I have an important test, I always wear my grandmother's locket as a **talisman** to give me confidence and help me do well.
9. In my family, turning the television on during a meal is practically considered a form of **sacrilege**, as we all value having time to catch up with one another.
10. The parents issued a **gambit** to their son: Finish your homework, or lose all television privileges for the week.

Choosing the Right Word

*Select the **boldface** word that better completes each sentence. You might refer to the passage on pages 24–25 to see how most of these words are used in context. Note that the choices might be related forms of the Unit words.*

1. In ancient Egypt, (**talismans, sacrileges**) with the image of a scarab beetle were considered sacred and believed to have healing and protective powers.
2. After years of failure to sell a single story, the young writer described himself bitterly as "a(n) (**myopic, avid**) collector of rejection slips."
3. The adoring fan regarded my negative comments about his favorite singer as tantamount to (**gambit, sacrilege**).
4. He is the kind of person who is concerned not with real moral values but simply with appearances and (**propriety, talismans**).
5. To the delight of the impatient graduates, the university president offered her comments at the commencement ceremony (**summarily, avidly**).
6. His methods were so complicated and his purposes so (**histrionic, devious**) that we were not sure if he was spying on the enemy or on us.
7. "I realize that this kind of financial (**gambit, sacrilege**) has its risks," she said, "but I expect it to pay off handsomely in the end."
8. Without even considering the new evidence that I was prepared to present, they (**deviously, summarily**) denied my appeal to reopen the case.
9. He regarded his Phi Beta Kappa key as a(n) (**talisman, animadversion**) that would open all doors and win him universal acceptance.
10. After the young actor's audition, the casting directors delivered a harsh evaluation of his overly (**histrionic, devious**) monologue.
11. I certainly do not claim that my performance in office was beyond criticism, but I deeply resent (**animadversions, proprieties**) on my honesty.
12. In an age when the United States has truly global responsibilities, we can ill afford leaders with (**myopic, avid**) points of view.

Completing the Sentence

Choose the word from the word bank that best completes each of the following sentences. Write the correct word or form of the word in the space provided.

animadversion	**devious**	**histrionic**	**propriety**	**summarily**
avid	**gambit**	**myopic**	**sacrilege**	**talisman**

1. Down in the main square, a hard-working peasant was selling charms and _______________ to ward off the evil eye.

2. In Grandmother's day, standards of _______________ required that a young lady wear a hat and gloves when she went out in public.

3. After the prisoner had been found guilty of treason, he was led before a firing squad and _______________ executed.

4. His pale face, hunched shoulders, and _______________ stare showed that he had spent his life poring over old books and documents.

5. My brother is such a(n) _______________ collector of toy soldiers that I sometimes think our house has been invaded by a pint-sized army.

6. In the eyes of most Americans, people who burn or spit on our flag are guilty of a kind of _______________.

7. Saying that "people who live in glass houses shouldn't throw stones" is not an effective response to their _______________ on your conduct.

8. To be really convincing on stage, an opera singer must possess both vocal and _______________ abilities.

9. On the return trip, we cut straight across the meadows rather than take the more _______________ path along the river.

10. Any book on chess strategy usually discusses the standard opening moves, such as the "knight's _______________."

End Set B

Synonyms

*Choose the word or form of the word from this Unit that is the same or most nearly the same in meaning as the **boldface** word or expression in the phrase. Write that word on the line. Use a dictionary if necessary.*

1. biased and **shortsighted** ____________________
2. was taken in by her **scheme** ____________________
3. an act of **desecration** ____________________
4. **ripple** in the current ____________________
5. completed the job with **alacrity** ____________________
6. **abruptly** resigned from the Cabinet ____________________
7. had **sneaky** intentions ____________________
8. a lucky **amulet** ____________________
9. memories of our **serene** beginnings ____________________
10. the **petitioner's** request for leniency ____________________
11. behaved with her usual **decorum** ____________________
12. the **vortex** of public opinion ____________________
13. **confronted** the thief at the door ____________________
14. swam in the **briny** water ____________________
15. set off by **provocative** language ____________________

Antonyms

*Choose the word or form of the word from this Unit that is most nearly opposite in meaning to the **boldface** word or expression in the phrase. Write that word on the line. Use a dictionary if necessary.*

1. a **reluctant** sports fan ____________________
2. endure **praise** from the principal ____________________
3. made a very **low-keyed** plea for mercy ____________________
4. took **secret** action to avoid a crisis ____________________
5. spoke in a **complimentary** tone ____________________

Writing: Words in Action

Write an essay about the completion of the subway and analyze the impact—both positive and negative—on individuals and businesses in New York City at the turn of the century. Use at least two details from the passage (pages 24–25) and three or more words from the Unit to support your view.

Vocabulary in Context

*Some of the words you have studied in this Unit appear in **boldface** type. Read the passage below, and then circle the letter of the correct answer for each word as it is used in context.*

Many Los Angeles old-timers cherish their streetcar mementos as **talismans**, and little wonder, for the city's streetcar system once provided fast, practical, cheap transportation to hundreds of thousands of daily commuters. Maps of the system in its **halcyon** era—the first decades of the twentieth century—show a network of lines covering the metropolitan region, even crossing the **brackish** waters of the Los Angeles River in several locations.

The demise of Los Angeles's streetcar system is the subject of intense debate. According to some, a consortium of business interests representing the automobile, oil, and tire industries conspired to buy up streetcar lines nationwide, dismantle the systems, and pave the way for their own products. And there is a certain amount of truth to this story. In 1945, a company called National City Lines—backed by investors such as General Motors and Standard Oil—purchased a major streetcar company, Los Angeles Railway. Harried commuters were soon riding in exhaust-spewing buses. Years later, an antitrust attorney used a Senate hearing to **accost** the directors of General Motors, arguing that the corporation's "destruction of electric transit systems across the country left millions of urban residents without an attractive alternative to automotive travel."

But Los Angeles's streetcars were probably doomed anyway. From the beginning, the streetcar lines were part of an **overt** strategy cooked up by land barons for selling homes in the city's suburbs. The strategy worked—Angelenos moved farther and farther away from downtown. Cars then changed everything. With cars came the inevitable traffic jams, and streetcars' **celerity** and popularity were forever lost. Los Angeles voters, it should be noted, quickly began supporting measures to build more highways.

---

1. A **talisman** is an object that serves as
a. a memory
b. a charm
c. an antique
d. a decoration

2. A **halcyon** era is
a. long past
b. debated
c. depressed
d. golden

3. Water that is **brackish**, as the Los Angeles River is said to be, is
a. murky
b. polluted
c. salty
d. slow-moving

4. The word **accost** most nearly means
a. anger
b. confront
c. litigate
d. question

5. An **overt** strategy is
a. not hidden
b. underhanded
c. self-serving
d. covert

6. A streetcar with **celerity** travels with
a. thrift
b. efficiency
c. comfort
d. rapidity

Read the following passage, taking note of the ***boldface*** *words and their contexts. These words are among those you will be studying in Unit 3. It may help you to complete the exercises in this Unit if you refer to the way the words are used below.*

Third Parties in American Politics

<Encyclopedia Entry>

The two-party system has been in effect since the **primordial** days of American politics and the Founding Fathers. At that time, the two opposing parties were known as the Federalists and the Anti-Federalists. Democrats and Republicans dominate United States politics now, but smaller third parties have addressed **substantive** issues, challenged the two-party orthodoxy, and **evinced** signs of success at local, state, and national levels.

Background and Perspective

A modern-day third-party candidate has yet to wrest the presidency from the Republicans or Democrats. However, many third-party positions have been adopted by the major parties, whose **propinquity** has been **decried** by voters who want clearer divisions.

Sometimes, after Democrats or Republicans have embraced the ideas of a third party, that third party has faded away. Other times—although not since the nineteenth century—a third party has become so powerful that it supplants one of the major parties. This happened in 1856 when the Republican Party, a third party at the time, replaced the Whig Party.

Some third parties have clear-cut platforms and strong nominees, while others have been criticized for **murky** views or **feckless** leadership or for having more **utopian** than real-world positions. Still others are essentially single-issue parties—like the Prohibition Party—known for its opposition to the sale or consumption of alcohol.

Significant Third Parties in U.S. History

The Know-Nothing Party This party rose with **unwonted** rapidity in the mid-1800s. Among other things, its leaders spread **nefarious** misinformation to increase opposition to Catholic immigration from countries such as Ireland and Germany. The name came about because members, when asked about the party's activities, **dissembled** and said they "knew nothing." The party shortly died out, but modern candidates **exhume** parts of its platform from time to time, for example, calling for restrictions on liquor sales.

Teddy Roosevelt and the Bull Moose Party In 1912, former President Theodore Roosevelt tried to win back the presidency by challenging incumbent William Howard Taft for the Republican nomination. Roosevelt lost, but a rolling stone gathers no moss, and he formed the Progressive Party, soon nicknamed the Bull Moose Party. This development split the Republican vote, and the Democrat, Woodrow Wilson, was elected President. Although Roosevelt, known for his colorful **verbiage** in speeches and **piquant** ideas, lost, much of his platform later became public policy.

A campaign ribbon from 1856 for the Know-Nothing Party

Teddy Roosevelt's Bull Moose Party captured the imagination of the voting public in 1912.

Recent Third-Party Candidates

Some contenders, like H. Ross Perot in 1992 and 1996 and Ralph Nader in two of his bids—in 2000 and 2004—won enough votes to give **credence** to the idea of a third party in the United States. Some have viewed third-party candidates as "spoilers": They cannot win, but they'll siphon off enough votes to impact the election.

H. Ross Perot This billionaire businessman and folksy populist threw his hat into the presidential ring in 1992 as a Reform Party candidate. He received almost 20 million votes, more than any other third-party candidate since Theodore Roosevelt in 1912.

Ralph Nader A trailblazing consumer advocate and four-time presidential candidate, Nader ran for President in 2000 on the Green Party ticket. Some Democrats feared he would draw votes from their candidate, Al Gore. Nader won just under 3 percent of the vote.

Legacy

The United States has the longest-surviving two-party system of any country. However, roughly one-third of voters today are not affiliated with either of the two major parties, and that number is growing. Many people are registering as Independents, which may signal an opportunity for the next third party.

Audio

For iWords and audio passages, go to **SadlierConnect.com**.

Definitions

Note the spelling, pronunciation, part(s) of speech, and definition(s) of each of the following words. Then write the appropriate form of the word in the blank space in the illustrative sentence(s) following.

1. credence (krēd′ əns)
(*n.*) belief, mental acceptance
The government and the public failed to give ____________________ to the reports of an impending water shortage.

2. dissemble (di sem′ bəl)
(*v.*) to disguise or conceal, deliberately give a false impression
The young man was unable to ____________________ his feelings and admitted to having committed the crime.

3. evince (i vins′)
(*v.*) to display clearly, to make evident, to provoke
The crowd did not ____________________ any signs of panic but moved in an orderly fashion to the nearest exits.

4. feckless (fek′ ləs)
(*adj.*) lacking in spirit and strength; ineffective, weak; irresponsible, unreliable
Although a ____________________ youth, he eventually matured into a hard-working and responsible citizen.

5. nefarious (nə fâr′ ē əs)
(*adj.*) wicked, depraved, devoid of moral standards
Brutus and Cassius hatched a ____________________ plot to assassinate Julius Caesar on the steps of the Roman Senate.

6. primordial (prī môr′ dē əl)
(*adj.*) developed or created at the very beginning; going back to the most ancient times or earliest stage; fundamental, basic
The ____________________ stages of most civilizations are founded on common needs met by common goals.

7. propinquity (prō piŋ′ kwə tē)
(*n.*) nearness in place or time; kinship
The ____________________ of the two cities has created a greater metropolitan area that in effect is one city.

8. substantive (səb′ stən tiv)
(*adj.*) real, having a solid basis; considerable in number or amount; meaningful and on topic
The candidate dismissed the silly questions but took the time to answer the most ____________________ ones.

9. unwonted (un wōn′ tid)

(*adj.*) not usual or expected; not in character

The listless student answered with ____________ spirit when the subject of military tactics was raised.

10. viscous (vis′ kəs)

(*adj.*) having a gelatinous or gluey quality, lacking in easy movement or fluidity

The varnish left a ____________ residue on the wood that was hard to remove.

Using Context

*For each item, determine whether the **boldface** word from pages 38–39 makes sense in the context of the sentence. Circle the item numbers next to the six sentences in which the words are used correctly.*

1. Although I didn't like the gift, I tried to **dissemble** my true feelings and express gratitude.
2. The cave paintings found in Lauscaux, France, which are estimated to be 20,000 years old, are famous examples of **primordial** artwork.
3. The team's recent winning streak lends **credence** to your prediction that it will reach the championship this year.
4. Today, spacecraft are exploring Jupiter; in the future, they will travel to the edge of the solar system and other **unwonted** regions of space.
5. No matter how many times we hear that joke, it is always sure to **evince** a hearty laugh from us.
6. The author was relieved to see that the editor's comments on the manuscript called for only minor changes, not **substantive** ones.
7. Tales about modern superheroes generally include villains with **nefarious** plans to take over an entire city or perhaps even the world.
8. We are learning about the culture and customs of Japan so that we can behave with **propinquity** when we travel there on our glee club tour.
9. The figure skater's **feckless** performance earned a perfect score from the judges.
10. Painters flocked to the island, attracted by the unique **viscous** light that bathed it early in the morning and late in the afternoon.

Choosing the Right Word

*Select the **boldface** word that better completes each sentence. You might refer to the passage on pages 36–37 to see how most of these words are used in context. Note that the choices might be related forms of the Unit words.*

1. The extraordinary musical talents of Wolfgang Amadeus Mozart (**evinced, dissembled**) themselves at an amazingly early age.

2. The (**feckless, primordial**) efforts of our new quarterback caused the team to lose.

3. Because the playwright had hurried through her first draft, she had to make (**substantive, nefarious**) changes as she revised the dialogue.

4. When life was easy he was all dash and confidence, but in times of trouble his essentially (**viscous, feckless**) character came to the fore.

5. The behavior of armies in wartime often evinces the (**substantive, primordial**) blood lust that civilized people have not yet fully overcome.

6. Despite all the reports of "miraculous" cures, you would be well advised to withhold (**propinquity, credence**) until the drug has been fully tested.

7. His (**viscous, unwonted**) interest in the state of my finances strengthened my suspicions that he was about to ask for a loan.

8. An accomplished hypocrite usually finds it very easy to (**dissemble, evince**) his or her true feelings as circumstances dictate.

9. The (**credence, propinquity**) of our ideas on handling the problem made it very easy for my colleague and me to produce the report in record time.

10. Trying to read your (**viscous, unwonted**) prose is just like trying to swim upstream through custard.

11. Members of Congress were relieved to learn that the current peace negotiations involve (**primordial, substantive**) discussion of key issues.

12. The United States is cooperating with the other nations of the world in an effort to check the (**feckless, nefarious**) trade in narcotics.

Completing the Sentence

Choose the word from the word bank that best completes each of the following sentences. Write the correct word or form of the word in the space provided.

credence	**evince**	**nefarious**	**propinquity**	**unwonted**
dissemble	**feckless**	**primordial**	**substantive**	**viscous**

1. Though diesel fuels are not as thick as motor oil, they are a good deal more ____________________ than regular gasoline.

2. In the hands of our hopelessly ____________________ producer, what should have been a surefire hit turned into a resounding fiasco.

3. Even at an early age, my sister ____________________ a strong interest in studying medicine.

4. An educated citizenry will not give ____________________ to wild charges of extremists seeking to undermine our political and economic system.

5. Since my apartment is in such close ____________________ to my office, I usually walk to work.

6. The NCAA has in recent years cracked down hard on such ____________________ practices as "shaving points."

7. Although Aimée is usually quiet in class, her contribution to our political discussion yesterday was ____________________.

8. I believe there is an overall design to the universe that has been visible ever since the first thing crawled out of the ____________________ ooze.

9. I have always regarded the man as something of a daredevil, but on this occasion he approached the problem with ____________________ caution.

10. Though I prefer to be as open and aboveboard as possible, I have learned that it is sometimes wiser or more tactful to ____________________.

End Set A

Definitions

Note the spelling, pronunciation, part(s) of speech, and definition(s) of each of the following words. Then write the appropriate form of the word in the blank space in the illustrative sentence(s) following.

1. cavort (kə vôrt′)
(*v.*) to romp or prance around exuberantly; to make merry
The actors in the musical ____________________ on stage.

2. decry (di krī′)
(*v.*) to condemn, express strong disapproval; to officially depreciate
Every arm of government and every educational institution should ____________________ bigotry in all its forms.

3. distraught (dis trôt′)
(*adj.*) very much agitated or upset as a result of emotion or mental conflict
The workforce became ____________________ in the wake of the 1929 stock market crash.

4. eulogy (yü′ lə jē)
(*n.*) a formal statement of commendation; high praise
The best friend and longtime law partner of the deceased delivered the ____________________ at the funeral.

5. exhume (eks hyüm′)
(*v.*) to remove from a grave; to bring to light
Suspecting foul play, the coroner issued an order to ____________________ the body immediately.

6. murky (mər′ kē)
(*adj.*) dark and gloomy, obscure; lacking in clarity and precision
Many visitors have claimed to see a mysterious creature in the ____________________ waters of Loch Ness in Scotland.

7. piquant (pē′ kənt)
(*adj.*) stimulating to the taste or mind; spicy, pungent; appealingly provocative
The chef was an expert in making those ____________________ dishes that are characteristic of South Indian cooking.

8. utopian (yü tō′ pē ən)
(*adj.*) founded upon or involving a visionary view of an ideal world; impractical
A number of American religious groups like the Shakers have built separate communities based on ____________________ schemes.

9. verbiage (vər′ bē ij) (*n.*) language that is too wordy or inflated in proportion to the sense or content, wordiness; a manner of expression

The contract was full of meaningless ____________ that seemed designed to confuse the layperson.

10. verdant (ver′ dənt) (*adj.*) green in tint or color; immature in experience or judgment

The tourists on safari traveled over the ____________ grasslands of Kenya in search of native wildlife.

Using Context

*For each item, determine whether the **boldface** word from pages 42–43 makes sense in the context of the sentence. Circle the item numbers next to the six sentences in which the words are used correctly.*

1. You have plenty of good ideas in your speech, but you should cut any **verbiage** that might distract people from hearing your key points.
2. After a brief respite from playing sports to let my muscles rest, I was ready to **exhume** all of my previous activities.
3. Although some employees disagreed with her opinions on certain matters, they respected her **verdant** experience, which gave her a lot of insight.
4. He was so **distraught** after losing his job that he could not focus on finding other employment.
5. When the harvest was bountiful, the villagers would **cavort** around the town square in celebration.
6. Your **utopian** plan for finding housing for all homeless people in the city may sound unachievable to some, but I know you'll find a way to make a true impact.
7. The season finale of the popular show will **decry** the identity of the anonymous character responsible for the crime.
8. Although he thinks he is original and innovative, his ideas are so **piquant** that I feel like I've heard them a thousand times before.
9. The article was well written, but its key points were **murky**, so it left readers with a lot of questions.
10. The **eulogy** given in memory of the activist on the anniversary of her death brought everyone in the audience to tears.

Choosing the Right Word

*Select the **boldface** word that better completes each sentence. You might refer to the passage on pages 36–37 to see how most of these words are used in context. Note that the choices might be related forms of the Unit words.*

1. From the deck of our luxury liner, we occasionally caught sight of schools of dolphins (**cavorting, decrying**) playfully in the waves.

2. In my opinion, the columnist's observations about contemporary media and popular culture are humorous and wonderfully (**piquant, distraught**).

3. The new mayor is a curious mixture of the hardheaded pragmatist and the (**utopian, murky**) reformer.

4. Far from being unpleasant, her slight foreign accent added an extra dash of spice to her already (**verdant, piquant**) personality.

5. The book has an interesting plot, but the author has practically smothered it in endless (**verbiage, eulogy**).

6. From the bridge, the rescue team could just make out the blurred image of a car beneath the (**murky, utopian**) waters of the river.

7. (**Exhumed, Distraught**) with grief, they sat motionless for hours, staring blankly into space.

8. The investigating committee (**decried, cavorted**) the use of substandard materials and slovenly workmanship in the housing project.

9. Plato's (**utopian, verdant**) description of the ideal society and its politics in *The Republic* exerted great influence on later philosophers like Aristotle.

10. Not surprisingly, the address was a notably evenhanded affair in which the speaker cleverly mixed (**eulogy, verbiage**) with admonition.

11. Unfortunately, the (**piquant, verdant**) hopes and aspirations of my youth have been somewhat blighted by the icy blasts of reality.

12. Though the work hadn't seen the light of day for over a century, a daring impresario (**cavorted, exhumed**) and staged it to great public acclaim.

Completing the Sentence

Choose the word from the word bank that best completes each of the following sentences. Write the correct word or form of the word in the space provided.

cavort	**distraught**	**exhume**	**piquant**	**verbiage**
decry	**eulogy**	**murky**	**utopian**	**verdant**

1. Such spices as red pepper make many of the sauces used in Cajun cooking delightfully ____________________.

2. The new chairman ____________________ what she called the "deplorable tendency of so many Americans to try to get something for nothing."

3. When news of the fire ran through town, ____________________ residents rushed to the scene of the blaze.

4. For as far as the eye could see, ____________________ fields of unripe corn swayed gently in the morning breeze.

5. Sadly, the ____________________ schemes of high-minded idealists usually founder on the rocks of practical realities.

6. He clothes his puny ideas in such highfalutin ____________________ that they resemble gnats in top hats and tails.

7. How could we draw any clear ideas from a talk that was so disorganized, confused in language, and generally ____________________?

8. When new evidence turned up in the case, the court ordered the coroner to ____________________ the victim's body and reexamine it.

9. When Bill was told that he had made the varsity wrestling team, he began to ____________________ around the gym like a young colt.

10. Every Memorial Day, the mayor delivers a(n) ____________________ extolling the selfless devotion of those who have died in defense of this country.

End Set B

Synonyms

*Choose the word or form of the word from this Unit that is the same or most nearly the same in meaning as the **boldface** word or expression in the phrase. Write that word on the line. Use a dictionary if necessary.*

1. feared for the **helpless** child ______________
2. an unwelcome **proximity** ______________
3. **primeval** history ______________
4. some **actual** doubt ______________
5. gave **credit** to the gossip ______________
6. a slightly **gummy** coating of wax ______________
7. tried to calm the **frantic** parents ______________
8. **played** in the wading pool ______________
9. **manifest** a reaction ______________
10. **idealistic** opinions about the world ______________
11. could not make out the **unclear** image ______________
12. **feigned** astonishment at the surprise party ______________
13. a **blossoming** garden ______________
14. delivered an emotional **testimonial** ______________
15. a **zesty** sauce ______________

Antonyms

*Choose the word or form of the word from this Unit that is most nearly opposite in meaning to the **boldface** word or expression in the phrase. Write that word on the line. Use a dictionary if necessary.*

1. the **brevity** of speechwriters ______________
2. **commend** the judge's decision ______________
3. **bury** the animal's remains ______________
4. surprised by his **unexceptional** anger ______________
5. had **virtuous** intentions ______________

Writing: Words in Action

Suppose you are a third-party candidate running for president in the next election. Write a brief essay about one issue you would focus on and its importance to you and to the country in general. Use details from the passage (pages 36–37) and three or more words from the Unit to support your view.

Vocabulary in Context

Some of the words you have studied in this Unit appear in ***boldface*** *type. Read the passage below, and then circle the letter of the correct answer for each word as it is used in context.*

Is it time to write the final **eulogy** of the electoral college, the system by which Americans elect their Presidents (and vice presidents)? Many citizens would be surprised to learn that their presidential votes do not go for the candidates themselves. Rather, votes go for state electors, who, in turn, cast votes for the candidates. Under the electoral college system—originally established by the Twelfth Amendment in 1804—most states require electors to vote for the candidate who wins the state vote, not the national vote. This requirement means that states that vote reliably for one party or the other become less influential during presidential campaigns. So candidates **cavort** endlessly across the small number of "battleground states," where the outcome is still up for grabs.

Today most Americans live in states that are largely ignored by presidential campaigns. Instead of proposing **substantive** agendas that appeal to a wide swath of Americans, candidates produce a **viscous** flow of political ads aimed at segments of voters who happen to reside in contested states. And the voters notice. Turnout for presidential elections is significantly lower in non-battleground states than in battleground states. This raises the possibility of a candidate winning the electoral college while losing the popular vote, something that has left some voters **distraught** more than once in US history.

Only the most **verdant** political observer would espouse a constitutional amendment to abolish the electoral college. A far more feasible approach may be the national popular vote compact. States simply need to enact legislation requiring their electors to vote for the candidate who wins the most votes nationwide. As soon as states representing 270 electoral votes (the winning number) have passed such legislation, the electoral college becomes irrelevant.

---

1. A **eulogy** is a statement of

a. intent
b. false praise
c. commendation
d. constructive criticism

2. The word **cavort**, most nearly means

a. prance around
b. travel over
c. campaign
d. fight

3. A **substantive** agenda is

a. difficult
b. heavy
c. meaningful
d. wide-ranging

4. A **viscous** flow of ads is

a. mean-spirited
b. honest
c. free-flowing
d. thick

5. **Distraught** voters are

a. imperturbable
b. upset
c. sad
d. disenfranchised

6. The word **verdant** most nearly means

a. savvy
b. deluded
c. immature in judgment
d. optimistic

Vocabulary for Comprehension

Part 1

*Read this passage, which contains words in **boldface** that appear in Units 1–3. Then choose the best answer to each question based on what is stated or implied in the passage. You may refer to the passage as often as necessary.*

Questions 1–10 are based on the following passage.

Gertrude Simmons was born in 1876 on the Pine Ridge Reservation of South Dakota and raised in a tepee until Quaker missionaries convinced her mother to send the girl to a missionary school in Indiana. Plunged into a foreign, regimented environment where she was forbidden to speak her language and forced to wear clothes that flaunted the **propriety** of her Sioux heritage, young Simmons was horrified. The avowed goal of the school was to assimilate American Indians into white society, but what Simmons witnessed was a **devious** strategy to destroy American Indian culture. Settlers had an **insatiable** need to conquer all things American Indian—not just their land, but also their customs, history, and spirit. Simmons would spend the rest of her life fighting attempts by mainstream society and the government to **arrogate** American Indian rights.

Missionary school undermined Simmons's relationship with her family. Her **propinquity** with other American Indian children helped the girl endure separation from her mother, a bedrock of Yankton Sioux values. But, the girl realized, it was her mother who had decided that she needed to be "acculturated" by white America. Her mother eventually converted to Christianity, a change that may have led Simmons to adopt the name Zitkala-Sa (Red Bird), from a dialect different than her family's dialect. Astute and fiercely intelligent, the girl excelled at school and became fluent in English. The assimilation of Simmons was thus successful. But it created a permanent rift between her and her people, and throughout Zitkala-Sa's life, her writing would **evince** the plight of a woman estranged from two cultures.

After graduating from college, Zitkala-Sa became a teacher at the infamous Carlisle Indian Industrial School in Pennsylvania, where she began writing the short stories and essays for which she is remembered today. Soon she clashed with the school's founder, Richard Henry Pratt, who termed her short stories "trash." Because of her outspoken defense of American Indian culture, Pratt **summarily** demoted her from her teaching position, and Zitkala-Sa made her way west, where she took a job as a clerk on the Standing Rock Reservation. There she met her husband. The couple moved to the Ute Reservation in Utah, and Zitkala-Sa's career as an activist commenced. As a correspondent for the Society of American Indians, she began advocating for legal reforms, employment of American Indians, redress of land settlements, and the preservation of American Indian history. When she was elected the secretary of the society, she moved to Washington, D.C.

Life in the nation's capital did nothing to dull Zitkala-Sa's quest for justice. She continued to **decry** the destruction of American Indian culture, and she leveled unrelenting attacks on corruption within the Bureau of Indian Affairs (even calling for the bureau's abolishment). Perhaps her greatest achievement came in 1924, when Zitkala-Sa and two coauthors published *Oklahoma's Poor Rich Indians: An Orgy of Graft and Exploitation of the Five Civilized Tribes, Legalized Robbery*. The book, which **substantiated** allegations of abuse and land swindles against American Indians by the federal government, is a powerful legacy of this American hero.

1. The primary purpose of the passage is to
A) provide an overview of the life of Zitkala-Sa.
B) explain why Zitkala-Sa felt estranged from two cultures.
C) give details about the origins of Zitkala-Sa's activism.
D) inform the reader about historical injustices against American Indians.

2. As it is used in line 9, "propriety" most nearly means
A) rights of property ownership.
B) primary rules of society.
C) standards of what is proper.
D) lost educational traditions.

3. What is the main point of the second paragraph (lines 22–41)?
A) Simmons depended on her friends at school and enjoyed their time together.
B) As a result of her time at missionary school, Simmons would never be completely at home with her Sioux family or within white society.
C) Simmons's sense of alienation drove her to succeed no matter what the cost, and that made her an outcast from society.
D) Simmons never looked back once she arrived at the missionary school.

4. Which choice provides the best evidence to support the answer to the previous question?
A) Lines 23–27 ("Her. . . values")
B) Lines 27–30 ("But, the girl . . America")
C) Lines 34–36 ("Astute. . . English")
D) Lines 37–41 ("But it created. . . cultures")

5. As it is used in line 24, "propinquity" most nearly means
A) similarity.
B) kinship.
C) nearness in place.
D) common language.

6. It can be inferred that the author refers to Simmons's use of the name Zitkala-Sa to
A) raise doubts about her authenticity.
B) highlight the difficult question of identity faced by American Indians.
C) show that her new name seemed to create distance between Simmons and her family.
D) explain that Gertrude Simmons and Zitkala-Sa are the same person.

7. The main purpose of the third paragraph (lines 42–65) is to provide
A) details about Zitkala-Sa's adult life.
B) an explanation of Zitkala-Sa's transition from school teacher to advocate.
C) a summary of Zitkala-Sa's activism.
D) a question about Zitkala-Sa's commitment to American values.

8. As it is used in line 68, "decry" most nearly means
A) officially depreciate.
B) call attention to.
C) describe.
D) condemn.

9. What point is made when the author says that the book *Oklahoma's Poor Rich Indians* is a "powerful legacy" (line 81) of Zitkala-Sa?
A) The book exposed government mistreatment of American Indians.
B) The book exemplified Zitkala-Sa's work fighting for American Indian rights.
C) Zitkala-Sa worked for years on the book.
D) Zitkala-Sa viewed the book as the capstone of her career.

10. Which of the following statements is supported by the passage as a whole?
A) Zitkala-Sa used her language skills and education to aid American Indians.
B) Zitkala-Sa completed a book of stories about American Indians in Oklahoma.
C) Zitkala-Sa refused to reunite with her mother at Pine Ridge Reservation.
D) Zitkala-Sa was so interested in politics that she moved to Washington, D.C.

Vocabulary for Comprehension

Part 2

*Read this passage, which contains words in **boldface** that appear in Units 1–3. Then choose the best answer to each question based on what is stated or implied in the passage. You may refer to the passage as often as necessary.*

Questions 1–10 are based on the following passage.

The future of farming, some would have us believe, lies in cities. The roofs of buildings can be turned into thousands of acres of arable land, helping metropolitan areas become more food self-reliant. More importantly, old warehouses and deserted factories can be converted into high-tech vertical farms, whose crops **emulate**—both in flavor and nutritional content—those grown in natural conditions. Anyone who walks into one of the new vertical farms will quickly see some advantages of this new form of agriculture. Since they are vertical, the urban farms use much less space than traditional farms. Giant stacks of trays, each filled with perfect rows of **verdant** lettuce, arugula, kale, spinach, and other leafy plants, rise to the ceiling. And because vertical farms are closed systems, they are not bothered by the normal pests and weeds, and farmers can therefore **eschew** pesticides and herbicides. Further, most of the water is recycled, allowing vertical farms to use far less water than traditional farms.

Vertical farms also have an important social component. Typically, the farms occupy old buildings in urban centers where good-paying jobs for people without college degrees are scarce. One venture in Newark, New Jersey, will include four vertical farms, the largest occupying an abandoned steel mill near the city center. When fully operational, the company will employ 78 seeders, harvesters, and inspectors. These positions are year-round, as vertical farms are not affected by downtime during winter. Jobs are not the only benefit for Newark residents. The owners view their business as a **gambit** in a wider movement to provide healthful, fresh produce to urban communities that have been underserved by retail grocery stores.

However, the idea that city farms can begin to replace America's rural counterparts may not be **tenable**. A basic reason is the production costs associated with energy. Vertical farms rely on massive systems of LED lighting to grow their plants. The newest generation of LED lights is remarkably efficient, allowing urban farmers to raise crops in record time while manipulating the plants to optimize certain flavors. (For example, by controlling LED exposure and nutrient levels, technicians can produce arugula that is more **piquant** than the same plant grown in soil.) But arrays of artificial lighting, no matter how efficient, are far more expensive than what powers traditional farms—free sunlight. This means that the produce grown by vertical farms is expensive. Not surprisingly, the industry's most **avid** supporters are chefs at high-end restaurants, who can afford to pay vertical farm prices.

Given the inherent problem of costly energy, it would be **myopic** to expect urban farms to spur some sort of food revolution. Observing the hype surrounding New York's new rooftop gardens, an architect decided to explore the city's full agricultural potential. Yes, he discovered, New York could become a self-reliant agricultural entity. Intensive, widespread vertical farming could feed the city. But the energy needed to build, heat, and light the entire operation would approach the output of 25 nuclear power plants—a staggering electricity bill. Vertical farms may be a good way to grow produce for urban niche markets, but the vision of agriculturally self-reliant cities is **utopian**.

1. It can reasonably be inferred that the author views the claim that the future of farming "lies in cities" (line 2) with
A) enthusiasm.
B) curiosity.
C) disdain.
D) skepticism.

2. It can reasonably be inferred that the author describes some of the advantages of vertical farms in lines 13–44 in order to
A) explain the next agricultural revolution.
B) point out why crops from vertical farms are worth considering.
C) provide a balanced assessment of the farms.
D) establish that vertical farms are more important than rooftop gardens.

3. As it is used in line 17, "verdant" most nearly means
A) green.
B) immature.
C) abundant.
D) healthy.

4. Which choice best summarizes the second paragraph (lines 26–44)?
A) The jobs in vertical farms are well-paid, year-round positions.
B) The social component of vertical farms is exaggerated.
C) Vertical farms create jobs and provide produce to urban communities.
D) Vertical farms are a good way to make use of abandoned buildings.

5. The author includes information on the energy costs of vertical farms in the third paragraph (lines 45–67) in order to
A) point out a drawback to LED lighting.
B) explain why vertical farms cannot fully replace traditional farms.
C) prove that produce from vertical farms can only ever have a limited clientele.
D) explain why they grow bland produce.

6. Which choice proved the best evidence for the answer to the previous question?
A) Lines 49–51 ("Vertical farms. . . plants")
B) Lines 55–59 ("For example. . . soil")
C) Lines 59–62 ("But arrays. . . sunlight")
D) Lines 64–67 ("Not. . .prices")

7. As it is used in line 65, "avid" most nearly means
A) desirous.
B) dedicated.
C) high-profile.
D) intensely eager.

8. As it is used in line 69, "myopic" most nearly means
A) lacking a realistic view.
B) nearsighted.
C) lacking discernment.
D) overly optimistic.

9. What point does the author make by including the last paragraph?
A) Cities could use vertical farms to supply all of their food.
B) Large-scale vertical farming would entail huge outlays for energy.
C) Vertical farming is, in the end, a dream.
D) Vertical farms supply certain markets.

10. Which best summarizes the passage?
A) The next agricultural revolution is urban farming.
B) Urban farms will not replace rural farms.
C) Vertical farms face technological and financial challenges.
D) Urban farming offers new ways to grow produce, but its scope is limited.

Synonyms

*From the word bank below, choose the word that has the same or nearly the same meaning as the **boldface** word in each sentence and write it on the line. You will not use all of the words.*

accost	**incendiary**	**propinquity**	**taciturn**
banal	**intransigent**	**reconnaissance**	**talisman**
brackish	**maelstrom**	**summarily**	**undulate**
carping	**pejorative**	**suppliant**	**utopian**

1. A transit workers' strike is certain if both sides in the contract dispute remain **unyielding**. ________________

2. Someone who is not a morning person is likely to be moody and **uncommunicative** if woken too early. ________________

3. Those dogs are being trained to help with special missions, particularly those having to do with rescue and **exploration**. ________________

4. The sailors tied down everything in sight and prepared to face the **turbulence** that was coming their way. ________________

5. As part of the renovation, the designer replaced the old, **insipid** still-life paintings with striking, original works from local artists. ________________

6. Sometimes opposites attract, but perhaps more often, **similarity** causes people to become close friends. ________________

7. Plato's most famous work, *Republic,* describes an **idealistic** society. ________________

8. The photographers waiting outside the building did not **approach** the movie star because they did not recognize her in her disguise. ________________

9. The scientists are studying the health of the organisms that live in the **saline** water. ________________

10. If you make an offer on that rare baseball card that is too low, you must be prepared for the dealer to **promptly** reject it. ________________

11. The rebel leader's **inflammatory** words roused the troops as they prepared for battle. ________________

12. I know perfectly well that reading **hypercritical** comments on social media is a total waste of time, but sometimes I can't help myself. ________________

Two-Word Completions

Select the pair of words that best completes the meaning of each of the following sentences.

1. The senator hoped his colleagues would find his ________________ argument about the deficit to be ________________.
a. germane ... murky
b. histrionic ... invidious
c. viscous ... nefarious
d. coherent ... tenable

2. From the top of the mountain that summer afternoon, I looked out on a(n) ________________ panorama of fields and pasturelands through which countless streams and rivulets ________________ like so many serpents slithering lazily across a carpet.
a. avid ... congealed
b. primordial ... cavorted
c. substantive ... exhumed
d. verdant ... undulated

3. Despite the somewhat strident ________________ of some professional critics and the inane ________________ of a few literary pedants, the work enjoyed a notable popular success.
a. gambits ... sacrilege
b. animadversions ... carping
c. verbiage ... eulogies
d. encomiums ... largesse

4. Someone with a ________________ nature is generally very good at ________________, while more honest people give off unconscious cues that they are not telling the truth.
a. ubiquitous ... strategizing
b. acquisitive ... decrying
c. distraught ... emulating
d. devious ... dissembling

5. Little did we realize, as we ________________ blithely on the beach during those ________________ and cloudless days of spring 1914, that the world was moving inexorably into the maelstrom of total war.
a. cavorted ... halcyon
b. emulated ... insatiable
c. belabored ... utopian
d. evinced ... piquant

6. For what must have been the first and only time in his life, the overly cautious general did not ________________ or vacillate but committed his troops to battle with ________________ celerity.
a. temporize ... unwonted
b. dissemble ... feckless
c. arrogate ... overt
d. carp ... myopic

7. Someone who is by nature as skeptical as I am usually refuses to give any ________________ to the kinds of wild allegations thrown about in an election until they have been ________________ by solid evidence.
a. celerity ... decried
b. credence ... substantiated
c. propriety ... eschewed
d. largesse ... exhumed

Idioms

In one of the letters about women's suffrage (see pages 12–13), the writer predicts that after Wyoming's decision to allow women to vote, other Western states and territories will "follow suit."

"Follow suit" is an idiom. An **idiom** is a group of words whose meaning is different from the literal meanings of each word considered individually. For example, "follow suit" means "do the same as has been done previously." Speakers and writers often use idioms to add interest and an air of informality to their style and tone. While it is sometimes possible to determine the meaning of an idiom from its context, you should memorize the meanings of common idioms. For others, you may need to consult a dictionary.

Choosing the Right Idiom

Read each sentence. Use context clues to figure out the meaning of each idiom in ***boldface****. Then write the letter of the definition for the idiom in the sentence.*

1. Because the Smiths suspected that the rental contract was not **on the up and up,** they refused to sign it. ______
2. Although we read the directions twice, we couldn't **make heads or tails of** them. ______
3. Any library **worth its salt** has a variety of both print and digital encyclopedias. ______
4. Although I once doubted I would make the varsity team, now I believe it is **in the cards.** ______
5. I was **fit to be tied** when the airline lost my suitcases. ______
6. The bride hoped that **down the line** the groom would begin helping her address the wedding invitations. ______
7. The homeowners and the real estate agent tried to remain polite, but they were clearly **at odds.** ______
8. To her older colleagues, the new personal trainer seemed **wet behind the ears** on her first day. ______
9. One recently hired employee left the engineering department last week for **greener pastures.** ______
10. After tiring in the first half of the race, Bryan and Phil got a **second wind** in the last few laps. ______

a. in disagreement
b. a better situation
c. deserving of respect
d. furious
e. understand
f. legal
g. in the future
h. renewed energy
i. inexperienced and young
j. likely to happen

Classical Roots

cred—to believe

The root *cred* appears in **credence** (page 38). The literal meaning is "belief," but the word now suggests a belief that is accepted. Some other words based on the same root are listed below.

accreditation	**credibility**	**creditor**	**credulity**
credentials	**creditable**	**credo**	**credulous**

From the list of words above, choose the one that corresponds to each of the brief definitions below. Write the word in the blank space in the illustrative sentence below the definition. Use an online or print dictionary if necessary.

1. references, testimonials, or other (usually written) evidence of identity or status ("that which provides a basis for belief")

The security guard demanded to see their ____________________ before they could enter the building.

2. official authorization or approval (often used in regard to academic affairs)

The college received ____________________ as an institution of higher learning.

3. a person or an organization to which money is owed

The bank denied her request for a loan when they saw that she had made late payments to a past ____________________.

4. worthiness of belief

At the hearing, a panel of experts questioned the ____________________ of the advertisement.

5. an undue readiness to believe; a lack of critical judgment

The wily con artists exploited their victim's ____________________.

6. a statement or summary of faith or fundamental belief; an authoritative statement of religious belief (*"I believe"*)

The ____________________ of our hiking club is "Take only pictures; leave only footprints."

7. inclined to believe very readily, gullible

The naïve young man seemed as ____________________ as a child.

8. bringing or deserving credit or honor

Despite limited rehearsal time, the cast did a(n) ____________________ job on that play.

*Read the following passage, taking note of the **boldface** words and their contexts. These words are among those you will be studying in Unit 4. It may help you to complete the exercises in this Unit if you refer to the way the words are used below.*

Reforming the Security Council

<Newspaper Editorial>

For more than a decade, diplomats and politicians the world over have sought to reform the United Nations Security Council. While everyone seems to agree that reform could increase the Council's effectiveness, there is less **concord** as to how to bring it about. Many nations favor changes that suit their own interests and **grouse** about their rivals' points of view. As the debate drags on, proposals for reform pile up like **flotsam** on the shore, each idea thwarted by a barrage of **mordant** objections. So the process of reform has proven less efficient than the Security Council itself, and hope for change threatens to **atrophy**.

The Security Council was created to serve as a **bastion** of peace and security in the world. It has the power to mediate disputes and to authorize peacekeeping operations, sanctions, and military action. Its members include representatives from fifteen nations, five of which hold permanent seats. A minimum of nine votes is required for the Council to pass a resolution, but the five permanent members have the lion's share of influence over important decisions. If any permanent member votes against a proposed measure, the resolution does not pass.

This veto power held by the permanent members is the chief source of the Council's inefficacy. When there is disagreement among permanent members, a single "no" vote is enough to prevent the Council from taking action. Just the threat of a veto can throw negotiations into **disarray**, holding the Council hostage to the slow workings of diplomacy. This cumbersome process prevents the Council from reacting quickly to the **exigencies**

A meeting of the UN Security Council

The UN building in New York City, as seen from the East River

of political crises. Accordingly, many critics claim it is **incumbent** upon reformers to amend the Council's voting procedures. Others demand that the number of non-permanent members be increased to limit the permanent members' power. While there is wisdom in both of these suggestions, debate as to how the U.N. can implement such measures remains **frenetic**, with no end to the **stratagems** by which each nation hopes to gain advantage.

An increasing number of critics have suggested doing away with permanent membership entirely and making all members of the Council temporary officials. While proponents of this reform may **glean** support from some corners, there is little chance of its coming to pass. The permanent members will not willingly give up their privileged positions: Since they have the power to veto the proposal, it is **ludicrous** to expect that such a resolution could ever be enacted. Moreover, permanent membership is designed to reflect the realities of global politics. In theory, permanent members consist of the nations that contribute the most **pecuniary** and military support to the U.N. and that have the greatest power to influence world affairs by diplomatic, economic, or other means.

That is not necessarily the case today. The list of permanent members was drawn up just after World War II and no longer reflects the balance of global power. The fortunes of many nations have changed, for better or worse, in the past six decades. To better reflect today's world, influential nations such as Germany and Japan should be made permanent members, along with emerging regional powers like India, South Africa, and Brazil. And the Council's voting process must be improved. Achieving these aims will require an unusual degree of compromise and **consummate** diplomatic tact, and there is no doubt that some nations will be **nettled** by the result. But the only alternative is to allow the Council to remain an ineffective institution—and this is an outcome that benefits no one.

Audio

For iWords and audio passages, go to **SadlierConnect.com.**

A UN peacekeeper monitors the border between Israel and Lebanon.

Definitions

Note the spelling, pronunciation, part(s) of speech, and definition(s) of each of the following words. Then write the appropriate form of the word in the blank space in the illustrative sentence(s) following.

1. atrophy (a′ trə fē)
(*n.*) the wasting away of a body organ or tissue; any progressive decline or failure; (*v.*) to waste away

The ____________ of the downtown business district began when two huge malls opened.

The patient's muscles have ____________.

2. concord (kän′ kôrd)
(*n.*) a state of agreement, harmony, unanimity; a treaty, pact, covenant

A spirit of ____________ was restored when the company compensated its employees.

3. disarray (dis ə rā′)
(*n.*) disorder, confusion; (*v.*) to throw into disorder

The burgled home was in a state of ____________.

If you leave the window open, a breeze may ____________ the papers on the desktop.

4. frenetic (frə net′ ik)
(*adj.*) frenzied, highly agitated

When a court order was issued, the social services department made a ____________ search for the missing report.

5. grouse (grau̇s)
(*n.*) a type of game bird; a complaint; (*v.*) to complain, grumble

The patient's latest ____________ was that he did not get any dessert with his dinner the night before.

Those who just stand around and ____________ about their low salaries are not likely to get raises.

6. incumbent (in kəm′ bənt)
(*adj.*) obligatory, required; (*n.*) one who holds a specific office at the time spoken of

Voting on election day is a duty ____________ on all Americans who value a democratic government.

The ____________ has the advantage when standing for reelection but does not have a guarantee of victory.

7. jocular (jäk′ yə lər)
(*adj.*) humorous, jesting, jolly, joking

After receiving the news that she was ahead in the polls, the candidate was in a delightfully ____________ mood.

8. mordant (môr′ dənt)
(*adj.*) biting or caustic in thought, manner, or style; sharply or bitterly harsh

The actor was upset by the ____________ criticism of the gossip columnist who seemed out to ruin his reputation.

9. pusillanimous (pyü sə lan′ ə məs)
(*adj.*) contemptibly cowardly or mean-spirited

It is often said that bullies, when tested, are the most ____________ people of all.

10. stratagem (strat′ ə jəm)
(*n.*) a scheme to outwit or deceive an opponent or to gain an end

The defense attorney used a clever ____________ to curry sympathy for her client.

Using Context

For each item, determine whether the boldface word from pages 58–59 makes sense in the context of the sentence. Circle the item numbers next to the six sentences in which the words are used correctly.

1. It was uplifting to hear the two choirs blend their voices in perfect **concord**.
2. The company was in decline, but now it is in a period of **atrophy**, with soaring growth.
3. It is better to work slowly and steadily and accomplish all your tasks than to work at a **frenetic** pace and quickly become exhausted.
4. The speaker's easygoing manner and **jocular** tone quickly put everyone in the audience at ease.
5. The children left their toy room in such **disarray** that it will take hours to clean up their mess.
6. Earth's rocky **stratagem** is about 25 miles deep in most places.
7. We determined that the **pusillanimous** smell was coming from a bag of rotting potatoes.
8. After winning the big game, the members of the team can be expected to happily **grouse** on the field and wave to the fans.
9. According to the rules of the election, an **incumbent** may run for a second term but not for a third.
10. Mark Twain, a writer known for his **mordant** sense of humor, once said, "It is better to keep your mouth closed and let people think you are a fool than to open it and remove all doubt."

Choosing the Right Word

*Select the **boldface** word that better completes each sentence. You might refer to the passage on pages 56–57 to see how most of these words are used in context. Note that the choices might be related forms of the Unit words.*

1. During the nineteenth century, it was fashionable to spend a few weeks in the fall hunting (**grouse, incumbents**), pheasants, and other game birds.
2. Before the ceremony began, we all bowed our heads and hoped for unity, peace, and (**concord, atrophy**) among all nations.
3. We were fascinated by the (**mordant, frenetic**) scene on the floor of the stock exchange as brokers struggled to keep up with sudden price changes.
4. The huge influx of wealth that resulted from foreign conquests led in part to the physical and moral (**atrophy, stratagem**) of the Roman ruling class.
5. The undisciplined puppy (**disarrayed, groused**) the boxes in the garage.
6. Of the ten Congressional seats in our state, only one was won by a new member; all the other winners were (**incumbents, concords**).
7. To feel fear in difficult situations is natural, but to allow one's conduct to be governed by fear is (**jocular, pusillanimous**).
8. Although most of the diners' comments were favorable, several (**grouses, concords**) about the soggy salads dismayed the chef.
9. The affairs of our city are in such (**disarray, atrophy**) that the state may have to intervene to restore some semblance of order.
10. What we need to cope with this crisis is not cute (**grouses, stratagems**) but a bold, realistic plan and the courage to carry it out.
11. I noticed with approval that his (**pusillanimous, mordant**) remarks were intended to deflate the pompous and unmask the hypocritical.
12. Do you really think that those (**jocular, frenetic**) remarks are appropriate on such a solemn occasion?

Completing the Sentence

Choose the word from the word bank that best completes each of the following sentences. Write the correct word or form of the word in the space provided.

atrophy	**disarray**	**grouse**	**jocular**	**pusillanimous**
concord	**frenetic**	**incumbent**	**mordant**	**strategem**

1. It was pleasant to see the usually quiet and restrained Mrs. Baxter in such a(n) ____________________ and expansive mood.

2. Almost every case of muscle or tissue ____________________ is the result of disease, prolonged disuse, or changes in cell nutrition.

3. People who are used to the unhurried atmosphere of a country town often find it hard to cope with the ____________________ pace of big-city life.

4. The purpose of our ____________________ was to draw in the safety so that Tom could get behind him to receive a long pass.

5. I have yet to meet an adult who did not ____________________ about the taxes he or she had to pay.

6. Most people regarded the government's attempt to avert a war by buying off the aggressor as not only shameful but ____________________.

7. The defeated army fled in such ____________________ that before long it had become little more than a uniformed mob.

8. It is ____________________ on all of us to do whatever we can to help our community overcome this crisis.

9. Peace is not just the absence of war but a positive state of ____________________ among the nations of the world.

10. Shakespeare's Timon of Athens is a disillusioned misanthrope who spends his time hurling ____________________ barbs at the rest of mankind.

End Set A

Definitions

Note the spelling, pronunciation, part(s) of speech, and definition(s) of each of the following words. Then write the appropriate form of the word in the blank space in the illustrative sentence(s) following.

1. bastion (bas′ chən) — (*n.*) a fortified place, stronghold

Contrary to popular belief, the military is not always a ______________ of political conservatism.

2. consummate (*v.*, kän′ sə māt; *adj.*, kən′ sə mət) — (*adj.*) complete or perfect in the highest degree; (*v.*) to bring to a state of completion or perfection

Michelangelo's paintings on the ceiling of the Sistine Chapel in the Vatican are works of ______________ artistry.

The lawyers could not ______________ the settlement until the two parties met face to face.

3. exigency (ek′ sə jən sē) — (*n.*, often *pl.*) urgency, pressure; urgent demand, pressing need; an emergency

He emphasized the ______________ of the situation by requesting the immediate dispatch of rescue teams.

4. flotsam (flät′ səm) — (*n.*) floating debris; unimportant or discarded material

After the two ships collided, the survivors clung to various pieces of ______________ and hoped for rescue.

5. glean (glēn) — (*v.*) to gather bit by bit; to gather small quantities of grain left in a field by the reapers

By means of painstaking investigation, the detectives will eventually ______________ the truth.

6. incarcerate (in kär′ sə rāt) — (*v.*) to imprison, confine, jail

They will ______________ the convicted felon at the state penitentiary.

7. ludicrous (lüd′ ə krəs) — (*adj.*) ridiculous, laughable, absurd

Her comment was so ______________ that we finally understood that she was joking.

8. nettle (net′ əl) — (*n.*) a prickly or stinging plant; (*v.*) to arouse displeasure, impatience, or anger; to vex or irritate severely

If you are pricked by a ______________, aloe cream will soothe and reduce the sting.

The principal was ______________ by the student's disrespectful behavior.

9. pecuniary (pi kyü′ nē er ē)
(*adj.*) consisting of or measured in money; of or related to money
The couple was forced by ________________ considerations to sell their large home and buy a smaller one.

10. recumbent (ri kəm′ bənt)
(*adj.*) in a reclining position, lying down, in the posture of one sleeping or resting
The tired toddlers were ________________ on the couch after playing all afternoon in the yard.

Using Context

*For each item, determine whether the **boldface** word from pages 62–63 makes sense in the context of the sentence. Circle the item numbers next to the six sentences in which the words are used correctly.*

1. No matter how many fancy restaurants I visit in my lifetime, I will always consider my father to be the **consummate** chef who can make my favorite dishes to perfection.

2. As she headed home from the office on Friday evening, she vowed to **glean** any stressful events experienced during the week until Monday morning.

3. The pink-and-yellow house with the odd-shaped roof is the most **pecuniary** building you will find in this town.

4. The jail was now overflowing with prisoners, so a temporary facility was set up to **incarcerate** the newly arrested suspects.

5. His only plan for vacation was to be **recumbent** on a lounge chair on the beach with a good book in hand.

6. Nothing can **nettle** me more than listening to the senseless banter of talk-show radio hosts early in the morning.

7. The relaxed pace of the security guards as they approached the event showed the **exigency** of the situation.

8. The library was once seen as a **bastion** of knowledge, but now so much information can be found online.

9. The improbable situations and **ludicrous** characters in this novel make it hard to take the story seriously.

10. You must collect and organize all of the **flotsam** you have scattered throughout this house before you are allowed to go out with your friends.

Choosing the Right Word

*Select the **boldface** word that better completes each sentence. You might refer to the passage on pages 56–57 to see how most of these words are used in context. Note that the choices might be related forms of the Unit words.*

1. In Victorian times, fashionable ladies (**gleaned, incarcerated**) their waists in tight corsets to achieve a chic "hourglass" figure.

2. It has been said that the only way to handle a (**nettle, bastion**), or any difficult problem, without being stung is to grasp it firmly and decisively.

3. In his 1907 painting *The Sick Child*, Edvard Munch's depiction of a (**ludicrous, recumbent**) adolescent creates a mood of despair.

4. At the city dump, we saw broken furniture, old appliances, and other (**flotsam, exigencies**) of the large city.

5. We were able to (**incarcerate, glean**) only a few shreds of useful information from his long, pretentious speech.

6. There are few things in life as (**recumbent, ludicrous**) as an unqualified person trying to assume the trappings of authority.

7. The only way we'll really be able to increase productivity is to offer our employees a few solid (**consummate, pecuniary**) incentives to work harder.

8. I have always regarded our schools and colleges as citadels of learning and (**bastions, flotsam**) against ignorance and superstition.

9. Comfortably (**recumbent, ludicrous**) in the shade of the elm tree, I watched the members of the football team go through a long, hard workout.

10. All that I needed to (**consummate, nettle**) the most important deal of my career was her signature on the dotted line.

11. Why did my grandparents feel it necessary to show the (**pecuniary, ludicrous**) photo of me dressed as a chicken to my new girlfriend?

12. A born leader is someone who can rise to the (**bastions, exigencies**) of any crisis that he or she may be confronted with.

Completing the Sentence

Choose the word from the word bank that best completes each of the following sentences. Write the correct word or form of the word in the space provided.

bastion	**exigency**	**glean**	**ludicrous**	**pecuniary**
consummate	**flotsam**	**incarcerate**	**nettle**	**recumbent**

1. The ________________ that we observed here and there in the harbor bore mute testimony to the destructive power of the storm.

2. Even critics of our penal system admit that as long as hardened criminals are ________________, they can't commit further crimes.

3. Since I had had only one year of high-school French, my attempts to speak that language on my trip to Paris were pretty ________________.

4. I regret that Nancy was ________________ by my unfavorable review of her short story, but I had to express my opinion honestly.

5. The ________________ of my present financial situation demand that I curtail all unnecessary expenses for at least a month.

6. As soon as he struck the opening chords of the selection, we realized that we were listening to a(n) ________________ master of the piano.

7. The high ground east of the river formed a natural ________________, which we decided to defend with all the forces at our disposal.

8. Despite all their highfalutin malarkey about helping the poor, I suspect that their interest in the project is purely ________________.

9. I get my best ideas while lying down; the ________________ position seems to stimulate my brain.

10. Though next to nothing is known about Homer, historians have been able to ________________ a few odd facts about him from studying his works.

End Set B

Synonyms

*Choose the word or form of the word from this Unit that is the same or most nearly the same in meaning as the **boldface** word or expression in the phrase. Write that word on the line. Use a dictionary if necessary.*

1. **craven** behavior ______________
2. **immured** for years in a dank dungeon ______________
3. remain calm through periods of **crisis** ______________
4. a longtime **bulwark** of resistance ______________
5. left **floating wreckage** in its wake ______________
6. **gripes** about every change in the routine ______________
7. live in **harmony** together ______________
8. **collected** tidbits of information ______________
9. an **official** up for reelection ______________
10. **prostrate** on a hospital bed ______________
11. a **witty** conversation ______________
12. **irks** her coworkers with senseless chatter ______________
13. received **financial** compensation ______________
14. the **sardonic** wit of the satirist ______________
15. the ill-conceived **ruse** ______________

Antonyms

*Choose the word or form of the word from this Unit that is most nearly opposite in meaning to the **boldface** word or expression in the phrase. Write that word on the line. Use a dictionary if necessary.*

1. at a **leisurely** pace ______________
2. the **inept** host ______________
3. a **poignant** statement ______________
4. **order** the leaves after raking ______________
5. enthusiasm that **developed** ______________

Writing: Words in Action

How does having power bring out the best or the worst in a person? Write an essay that explains your opinion, using examples from your reading (refer to pages 56–57) and your own experience and observations to support your ideas. Write at least three paragraphs, and use three or more words from this Unit.

Vocabulary in Context

Some of the words you have studied in this Unit appear in ***boldface*** *type. Read the passage below, and then circle the letter of the correct answer for each word as it is used in context.*

On January 1, 1942, less than a month after the attack on Pearl Harbor, Hawaii, President Franklin D. Roosevelt brought representatives of all 26 nations at war with the Axis powers (Japan, Germany, and Italy) to Washington, D.C. In the **exigency** of the moment, Roosevelt, whose mind was never **recumbent** even in peacetime, looked ahead. His aim was to have them all sign the Atlantic Charter. He and British Prime Minister Winston Churchill had written it in August 1941. Signatories would commit to the Charter's eight "common principles" for the preservation of peace in the postwar world. There was to be nothing **pusillanimous** or **jocular** about the agreement. Signing nations agreed to renounce territorial expansion; to pursue international free trade and the freedom of the oceans; to free wrongly **incarcerated** persons; and to promote international standards for labor conditions, economic fairness, and welfare. Finally, all signatories would commit to restoring self-government to countries occupied during the war. The signed document, called the Declaration by United Nations, expressed a vision of a peaceful postwar world.

The idea of a peaceful world was a topic again at the Quebec Conference of August 1943. "A general international organization, based on the principle sovereign equality of all nations," was proposed in October 1943 at the Foreign Ministers' Conference in Moscow. In November 1943, President Roosevelt and Soviet Premier Josef Stalin met in Tehran and agreed to a general assembly of member states. At the Yalta Conference (Crimea) in February 1945, Roosevelt, Churchill, and Stalin achieved **concord** over the crucial question of who would belong to the Security Council. From April to June 1945 representatives of 50 member nations worked together in San Francisco to create the United Nations Charter. When it was complete, the Charter bore a remarkable similarity to the Atlantic Charter.

---

1. The word **exigency** most nearly means
- **a.** crisis
- **b.** thoughtlessness
- **c.** opportunity
- **d.** prism

2. To be **recumbent** is to be
- **a.** insolent
- **b.** alert
- **c.** inactive
- **d.** exhausted

3. An action that is **pusillanimous** is
- **a.** forward-looking
- **b.** lazy
- **c.** mean-spirited
- **d.** misleading

4. An action that is **jocular** is
- **a.** humorous
- **b.** ironic
- **c.** serious
- **d.** threatening

5. **Incarcerated** people are
- **a.** innocent
- **b.** collateral damage
- **c.** kept in the dark
- **d.** in prison

6. When **concord** is achieved,
- **a.** there is agreement
- **b.** hope reigns supreme
- **c.** people have freedom
- **d.** people are disbelieving

Read the following passage, taking note of the ***boldface*** *words and their contexts. These words are among those you will be studying in Unit 5. It may help you to complete the exercises in this Unit if you refer to the way the words are used below.*

What Is Pop Art?

<Essay>

Roy Lichtenstein's *In the Car,* 1963, looks like a comic strip but measures 30 x 40 in.

What is pop art? The simple answer: Art based on popular culture. Beginning in the mid-1950s and continuing for more than a decade, pop artists borrowed images directly from everyday popular culture. Drawing upon this seemingly **mundane** content, pop artists created bold, overpowering images. With great **acuity**, their canvases detailed such familiar things as comic strips, American flags, race cars, popular movie stars, and even boxes of laundry detergent.

In many ways, pop art was a reaction to abstract expressionism, the dominant style of painting during the 1940s and 1950s. Abstract expressionist paintings were nonrepresentational; they did not **delineate** objects directly. Instead, artists used abstract shapes and **nuances** in color to express personal ideas and feelings. Pop artists viewed abstract expressionism as elitist—too **esoteric** to be appreciated by most museumgoers. In response, they returned to representational art. This was a time when consumerism was booming in the United States and advertising had become **ubiquitous**. So the world around the pop artists became a **fecund** source of images.

At first, pop art **garnered** much negative criticism. Some critics complained that pop art's **penchant** for reproducing existing images—such as painting a portrait of a can of soup—was too easy. Others claimed the pop artist's love of commercial images **enervated** traditional

Warhol, Andy (1928–1987). *Vegetarian Vegetable from Campbell's Soup II*. 1969. Screenprint, $35\frac{1}{8}$ x $23\frac{1}{16}$ in. Gift of Mr and Mrs Peter Eider-Orley, 1972 (1972.724.3). The Metropolitan Museum of Art, New York, NY.

artistic values. A few critics even implied that pop art was **depraved**, or at least was devoid of aesthetic principles. Pop artists dismissed these arguments as so much **sophistry**. Why should traditional art be **hallowed** and commercial art be dismissed as vulgar? Was it a declaration of truth or a mere **fiat** when a critic pronounced one piece art and another trash?

No doubt reminding themselves that beauty is in the eye of the beholder, pop artists ignored the critics and continued to explore the relationship between the two types of art, playing around with commercial images and presenting them as works of art. Roy Lichtenstein, for example, chose comic strips as his main subject. Reproducing all the **idiosyncrasies** of this format, including voice balloons and printing dots, he chose frames that showed violent action or sentimental romance. The images, enlarged to monumental size and completely out of context, took on a new significance.

Andy Warhol is **reputed** to have eaten soup for lunch every day for twenty years. Perhaps that explains why he, the best-known of the pop artists, first became famous for his images of soup cans and other consumer products. Later, glamour and fame became a central theme of his work, and he produced **sumptuous** silkscreens of celebrities, such as Marilyn Monroe and Elvis Presley. Thanks to an **overweening** desire for publicity, Andy Warhol helped make pop art a household term, and he became one of the wealthiest artists of all time.

Pop art sculptors were also active, again taking consumer products as their starting point. Claes Oldenburg stuffed and painted cloth to produce giant hamburgers, toothpaste tubes, and ice cream bars. Like so much pop art, Oldenburg's "soft sculptures" remind us that, in pop art, the ordinary things of life become strange and things that we take for granted are seen anew, as if for the first time.

Pop art outlived its critics, and today, a half century later, its seriousness is not in doubt. As a movement, pop art ended, but not before greatly expanding the range of subjects, attitudes, and techniques available to all artists. Thanks to the pop artists, younger generations of painters, sculptors, and photographers now explore the world in more imaginative and thought-provoking ways.

Audio

For iWords and audio passages, go to **SadlierConnect.com.**

Definitions

Note the spelling, pronunciation, part(s) of speech, and definition(s) of each of the following words. Then write the appropriate form of the word in the blank space in the illustrative sentence(s) following.

1. delineate (di lin′ ē āt) — (*v.*) to portray, sketch, or describe in accurate and vivid detail; to represent pictorially

The architects will ____________ the main features of their plan at the next client meeting.

2. esoteric (es ə ter′ ik) — (*adj.*) intended for or understood by only a select few, private, secret

The fraternity developed a set of ____________ rites that had to be performed by anyone seeking membership.

3. fiat (fē ət) — (*n.*) an arbitrary order or decree; a command or act of will or consciousness

The ruler instituted several new ____________.

4. figment (fig′ mənt) — (*n.*) a fabrication of the mind; an arbitrary notion

The silhouette of a man on the porch was a mere ____________ of your overheated imagination.

5. hallow (hal′ ō) — (*v.*) to set apart as holy or sacred, sanctify, consecrate; to honor greatly, revere

In the Gettysburg Address, Lincoln ____________ the battlefield on which the Union soldiers fought and died.

6. idiosyncrasy (id ē ə siŋ′ krə sē) — (*n.*) a peculiarity that serves to distinguish or identify

The fact that the plurals of some nouns are formed irregularly is an ____________ of English grammar.

7. mundane (mən dān′) — (*adj.*) earthly, worldly, relating to practical and material affairs; concerned with what is ordinary

The painter left all ____________ concerns to her sister while she single-mindedly pursued her artistic goals.

8. nuance (nü′ äns) — (*n.*) a subtle or slight variation (as in color, meaning, quality), delicate gradation or shade of difference

In his writing, the poet paid close attention to every ____________ of meaning in the words he chose.

9. reputed (ri pyüt′ id)
(*adj.*) according to reputation or general belief; having widespread acceptance and good reputation; (*part.*) alleged

Although he is the ____________________ head of a crime syndicate, he has never spent time in jail.

10. sumptuous (səmp′ chü əs)
(*adj.*) costly, rich, magnificent

The ____________________ feast honoring the king's birthday was followed by musical entertainment.

Using Context

*For each item, determine whether the **boldface** word from pages 70–71 makes sense in the context of the sentence. Circle the item numbers next to the six sentences in which the words are used correctly.*

1. The traveler, a **reputed** spy, was being tracked and watched by the government agents carefully.
2. My video will clearly **delineate** the process of making a simple circuit using a battery, a small bulb, and some wire.
3. A low wooden door and a creaky set of stairs led to the dark, **sumptuous,** empty basement.
4. The article in the physics journal was so **esoteric** that I could not even understand the title.
5. Each king commanded a powerful **fiat** made up of thousands of well-armed troops.
6. The sacrifices made by the soldiers who died here will forever **hallow** these World War II battlefields.
7. Because I prepared and practiced my speech with great diligence and **idiosyncrasy**, I was comfortable delivering it to the audience.
8. Shopping in a large, modern supermarket can be a **mundane** task, but shopping at an outdoor farmer's market is truly a feast for the senses.
9. It would be wise to install fencing around your garden if you want to guard against the **nuance** of critters ravaging your vegetables.
10. The narwhal, an Arctic whale known as "the unicorn of the sea," might seem like a **figment** of the imagination, but it is, in fact, quite real.

Choosing the Right Word

*Select the **boldface** word that better completes each sentence. You might refer to the passage on pages 68–69 to see how most of these words are used in context. Note that the choices might be related forms of the Unit words.*

1. Few writers have J. D. Salinger's remarkable ability to (**delineate, hallow**) the emotions and aspirations of the average teenager.

2. In a democracy, the government must rule by persuasion and consent—not by mere (**fiat, figment**).

3. He means well, but we cannot tolerate his highly (**idiosyncratic, esoteric**) behavior in an organization that depends on discipline and teamwork.

4. The conversation between the computer programmers was so (**esoteric, sumptuous**) that I wasn't sure they were speaking English.

5. Weary of her (**mundane, reputed**) day-to-day life, the woman embarked on a summer-long bicycle adventure across the continental United States.

6. Two synonyms are rarely exactly the same because (**fiats, nuances**) of tone or applicability make each of the words unique.

7. In that rarefied atmosphere, I was afraid to ask about anything quite so (**sumptuous, mundane**) as the location of the rest room.

8. A true sign of intellectual maturity is the ability to distinguish the (**figments, nuances**) of wishful thinking from reality.

9. We will never abandon a cause that has been (**delineated, hallowed**) by the achievements and sacrifices of so many noble people.

10. The (**sumptuous, mundane**) banquet was a pleasant change of pace from the spartan fare to which I had become accustomed.

11. The alert defense put up by our team completely neutralized our opponents' (**reputedly, sumptuously**) unstoppable passing attack.

12. The majority of the population was controlled by the (**nuance, fiat**) of the smaller, more powerful group of people.

Completing the Sentence

Choose the word from the word bank that best completes each of the following sentences. Write the correct word or form of the word in the space provided.

delineate	**fiat**	**hallow**	**mundane**	**reputed**
esoteric	**figment**	**idiosyncrasy**	**nuance**	**sumptuous**

1. There is quite a difference between the austere furnishings of my little apartment and the ____________________ accommodations of a luxury hotel.

2. During the eleven years of his "personal rule," King Charles I bypassed Parliament and ruled England by royal ____________________.

3. Music can often express a(n) ____________________ of mood or feeling that would be difficult to put into words.

4. Most people I know are so busy dealing with the ordinary problems of life that they have no time for ____________________ philosophical speculation.

5. The artist's sketch not only ____________________ the model's appearance accurately, but also captured something of her personality.

6. "Your suspicion that I am constantly making fun of you behind your back is a mere ____________________ of your overheated brain," I replied.

7. The man is ____________________ to have mob connections, but so far no one has actually substantiated the allegation.

8. The ground in which those soldiers are buried was ____________________ by the blood they shed on it.

9. May I interrupt this abstruse discussion and turn your attention to more ____________________ matters—like what's for dinner?

10. His constant use of the word *fabulous*, even for quite ordinary subjects, is a(n) ____________________ that I could do without.

End Set A

Definitions

Note the spelling, pronunciation, part(s) of speech, and definition(s) of each of the following words. Then write the appropriate form of the word in the blank space in the illustrative sentence(s) following.

1. acuity (ə kyü′ ə tē)
(*n.*) sharpness (particularly of the mind or senses)
The ____________ of most people's hearing diminishes as they grow older.

2. depraved (di prāvd′)
(*adj.*) marked by evil and corruption, devoid of moral principles
Oscar Wilde's novel *The Picture of Dorian Gray* is about a ____________ man whose portrait reveals his wickedness.

3. enervate (en′ ər vāt)
(*v.*) to weaken or lessen the mental, moral, or physical vigor of; enfeeble, hamstring
Unfortunately, the great musician's mind was ____________ by disease in the last decade of her life.

4. fecund (fek′ und)
(*adj.*) fruitful in offspring or vegetation; intellectually productive
The remarkably ____________ mind of Albert Einstein produced theories that revolutionized the science of physics.

5. garner (gär′ nər)
(*v.*) to acquire as the result of effort; to gather and store away, as for future use
Over the years, the writer was able to ____________ some wisdom that she passed on to others in her books.

6. ignominy (ig′ nə min ē)
(*n.*) shame and disgrace
He went from glory to ____________.

7. overweening (ō vər wē ′niŋ)
(*adj.*) conceited, presumptuous; excessive, immoderate
It was the ____________ confidence of the candidate that prevented her from acknowledging her weaknesses.

8. penchant (pen′ chənt)
(*n.*) a strong attraction or inclination
A teacher with a ____________ for belaboring the obvious is bound to be boring.

9. sophistry (säf′ ə strē) (*n.*) reasoning that seems plausible but is actually unsound; a fallacy

The couple was beguiled into buying a bigger house than they needed by the clever ____________ of the broker.

10. ubiquitous (yü bik′ wə təs) (*adj.*) present or existing everywhere

The ____________ eye of the TV camera threatens to rob citizens of any sense of privacy.

Using Context

*For each item, determine whether the **boldface** word from pages 74–75 makes sense in the context of the sentence. Circle the item numbers next to the six sentences in which the words are used correctly.*

1. I planned to **garner** interest in my new club by handing out flyers, putting up posters, and providing refreshments during the meetings.
2. The protester attempted to **enervate** the attention of passersby by speaking into a megaphone, but he remained unnoticed by most people.
3. Researchers say that reading and completing crossword puzzles can help people maintain their mental **acuity** as they age.
4. She shows **sophistry** in her manner and dress, but I feel like a bumbling oaf in comparision.
5. The puppy had a **penchant** for stealing the children's toys and chewing them to bits.
6. The cruel and **depraved** activities of Dorian Gray are not evident in his own appealing countenance but are recorded supernaturally on his portrait, which he keeps locked away.
7. We were disappointed when she could not make the brainstorming meeting, as her **fecund** mind is always bursting with new and original ideas.
8. The excitement about the championship was so **ubiquitous** that one could hardly walk down the street without hearing people talk about the event.
9. I understand being concerned for the well-being of your child, but that mother's presence is so **overweening** that she can only be described as a "helicopter parent."
10. He had many questions about the lecture, but he waited to speak to the teacher after class because he did not want to display his **ignominy** about the subject to everyone.

Choosing the Right Word

*Select the **boldface** word that better completes each sentence. You might refer to the passage on pages 68–69 to see how most of these words are used in context. Note that the choices might be related forms of the Unit words.*

1. Cleopatra took her own life rather than suffer the (**acuity, ignominy**) of being led through the streets of Rome in chains.

2. Like a true fanatic, he considers anyone who disagrees with him on any issue to be either feebleminded or (**depraved, ubiquitous**).

3. Someone with a pronounced (**penchant, ignominy**) for saying the wrong thing might justly be described as a victim of "foot-in-mouth" disease.

4. Scandal and corruption may so (**enervate, garner**) an administration that it can no longer function effectively.

5. How I'd love to knock the wind out of the sails of that lout's (**fecund, overweening**) conceit!

6. Probably no complaint of young people is more (**ubiquitous, depraved**) than "My parents don't understand me!"

7. I appreciate all those kind expressions of gratitude for my services, but I had hoped also to (**garner, enervate**) some cash.

8. It is only in superior mental powers, not in physical strength or (**penchant, acuity**) of the senses, that human beings surpass other living things.

9. Your language is indeed clever and amusing, but your argument is nothing but a piece of outright (**sophistry, fecundity**).

10. Given my (**penchant, acuity**) for spicy food, I should enjoy the cayenne pepper.

11. Her imagination is like a (**fecund, depraved**) field in which new ideas spring up like so many ripe ears of corn.

12. Eight White Sox players in the 1919 World Series were banned from baseball for throwing games and forced to live with the (**sophistry, ignominy**) of their actions.

Completing the Sentence

Choose the word from the word bank that best completes each of the following sentences. Write the correct word or form of the word in the space provided.

acuity	**enervate**	**garner**	**overweening**	**sophistry**
depraved	**fecund**	**ignominy**	**penchant**	**ubiquitous**

1. Beneath the man's cultivated manner and impeccable grooming there lurked the ____________________ mind of a brutal sadist.

2. You may have many good traits, but I do not admire your ____________________ for borrowing things and failing to return them.

3. American-style fast-food shops have gained such popularity all over the world that they are now truly ____________________.

4. Analysis will show that his "brilliant exposition" of how we can handle the pollution problem without cost to anyone is sheer ____________________.

5. The passing years lessened her physical vigor but in no way diminished the ____________________ of her judgment.

6. The phonograph is but one of the wonderful new devices that sprang from the ____________________ mind of Thomas Edison, our most prolific inventor.

7. I was so ____________________ by the oppressive heat and humidity of that awful afternoon that I could barely move.

8. He was a changed young man after he suffered the ____________________ of expulsion from West Point for conduct unbecoming a gentleman.

9. The marathon not only brought in huge sums of money for Africa's starving masses, but also ____________________ much sympathy for their plight.

10. His ____________________ sense of superiority dominates his personality in much the same way as his beetling brow dominates his face.

End Set B

Synonyms

*Choose the word or form of the word from this Unit that is the same or most nearly the same in meaning as the **boldface** word or expression in the phrase. Write that word on the line. Use a dictionary if necessary.*

1. known for the **keenness** of her wit ________________
2. sought **occult** knowledge in ancient books ________________
3. **collect** more evidence ________________
4. their **omnipresent** sense of dread ________________
5. the **dishonor** of plagiarism ________________
6. known for his **propensity** for exaggeration ________________
7. a pond **fertile** with fish ________________
8. an **eccentricity** of speech ________________
9. tricked by **specious reasoning** ________________
10. the latest **creation** of his imagination ________________
11. a **supposed** heir to a huge fortune ________________
12. the **degenerate** thief ________________
13. as a result of a general **edict** ________________
14. a subtle **distinction** ________________
15. **depicted** the view from the balcony ________________

Antonyms

*Choose the word or form of the word from this Unit that is most nearly opposite in meaning to the **boldface** word or expression in the phrase. Write that word on the line. Use a dictionary if necessary.*

1. **defiled** by graffiti ________________
2. a man of **modest** aspirations ________________
3. **invigorated** by the heat ________________
4. the **otherworldly** side of life ________________
5. made a **meager** meal ________________

Writing: Words in Action

Is some art better than other art, or is the quality of a work of art just a matter of personal taste? What makes good art good, and bad art bad? Write an essay explaining your viewpoint. Support your ideas with details from your reading (refer to pages 68–69), and use three or more words from this Unit.

Vocabulary in Context

Some of the words you have studied in this Unit appear in ***boldface*** *type. Read the passage below, and then circle the letter of the correct answer for each word as it is used in context.*

Born in Atlantic City in 1917, Jacob Lawrence's family was originally from South Carolina. His family was part of the Great Migration of African Americans who fled the **ignominy** of enforced segregation in the South for better opportunities in the North. Lawrence attended art workshops at Utopia Children's House and the Harlem Art Workshop, where he was taught by Charles Alston, a **reputed** Harlem Renaissance artist and teacher. Lawrence also immersed himself in all elements of life in Harlem, from the profound to the **mundane**, and he drew much of what he saw.

In 1938, Lawrence received a scholarship to the American Artists School in New York, where he would **garner** wide attention for his bold use of color to **delineate** scenes of African American life. During this time, he also began creating narrative series—a narrative series involves creating 30 or more pieces on one subject. In 1941, he completed his most famous narrative series, *The Migration Series*. Many of the vibrant panels, which were not based on any **figment** of Lawrence's imagination but on the experiences of his family and the memories of people in his community, were exhibited at Downtown Gallery in 1942, making Lawrence the first African American artist to join the gallery and catapulting him into the national spotlight. Though Lawrence died in 2000, his work lives on in approximately 200 museum collections and on murals from Chicago to New York City.

---

1. The word **ignominy** most nearly means
a. mistreatment
b. oppression
c. disgrace
d. obligation

2. The word **reputed** most nearly means
a. likeable
b. highly regarded
c. well-educated
d. savvy

3. 3. A portrait of **mundane** life in Harlem would show
a. daily routines
b. bright colors
c. natural beauty
d. vivid detail

4. If you **garner** attention you
a. ignore it
b. discover it
c. squander it
d. acquire it

5. To **delineate** scenes, as Lawrence did, is to
a. modify their appearance
b. portray them accurately
c. render abstractions
d. draw on a surface

6. A **figment** is a(*n*)
a. fabrication
b. careful plan
c. ingenious invention
d. lofty achievement

UNIT 6

Read the following passage, taking note of the ***boldface*** *words and their contexts. These words are among those you will be studying in Unit 6. It may help you to complete the exercises in this Unit if you refer to the way the words are used below.*

Your Papers, Please

<Debate>

Today's debate question is:
Should every citizen of the United States be required to have a national identity card?

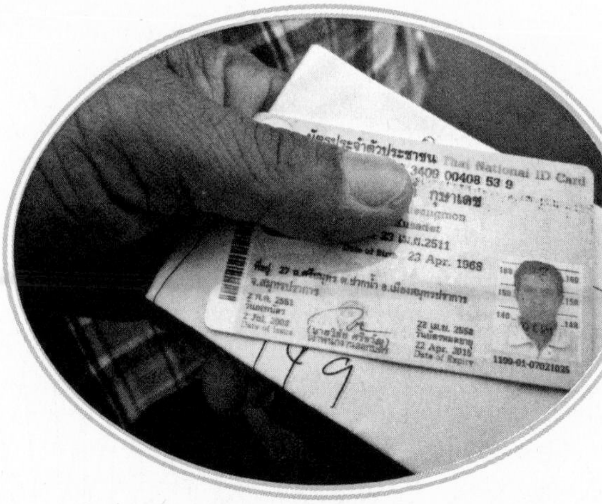

Tessa: The United States should implement a national identity card system without delay. Failure to do so would make the government **derelict** in its duty to protect citizens, as well as constitute a **travesty** of common sense. The most compelling argument favoring national ID cards is the crucial, ongoing effort to forestall any terrorist attacks against the United States. Advocates of national ID cards have noted with **perspicacity** that our existing system of **surveillance** has been proved inadequate and has failed in the past to detect the **complicity** of the terrorists in plots against the Unites States.

Tyrone: All that glitters is not gold, Tessa, and establishment of a national ID card would be an **abject** surrender of civil liberties and our citizens' right to privacy. At the risk of sounding **testy**, I firmly dispute the implicit assumption that an ID card system would have foiled previous terrorist attacks. That conjecture is an illusion in this high-tech world, where forgery, hacking, and identity theft might well have equipped terrorists with fake cards.

Tessa: I believe a national ID card would have several **indubitable** benefits, Tyrone. First, it would offer consistency, in contrast to the varying requirements of the states for the issue of driver's licenses. Second, an ID card system could be administered with **equity**. Despite the **diatribes** of privacy advocates against such a system, an effective ID card setup could operate with only five basic elements: name, address, Social Security number, photograph, and a finger or retinal print matching a chip on the card. Even a civil liberties **neophyte** would hesitate before raising an **indictment** of such requirements.

Tyrone: Tessa, people's right to privacy is the most important **motif** in my critique of a national ID card system, as there are numerous unresolved questions about the elements, requirements, and circumstances of an ID card program. All these questions would affect privacy: Would the program be voluntary or mandatory, for example? Who could lawfully demand presentation of the card, and on what occasions? Should the card be local, federal, or international? How much information could the government collect?

To ignore the risk of a slippery slope here would be **inane**. In the information age, everyone knows the extent to which giant institutions tend to assemble more and more data on citizens, sometimes for illegitimate purposes.

Tessa: I have several more arguments, Tyrone—the first of which is with a national ID card system concerns about racial and ethnic profiling would no longer be **moot**, because such concerns would be nullified by the uniformities of the card system. **Intermittent** harassment of minority groups would thus in all likelihood decline. Finally, many other countries, especially in Europe, use national ID cards successfully, so why not here?

Tyrone: A national ID card system would grant a single institution, the federal government, **plenary** powers to accrue information on all American citizens, so the potential for abuse is discernible. Contrary to your assertion, Tessa, racial profiling might actually increase. In other parts of the world with this system, the police are often entitled to demand presentation of the card on the threat of arrest. The misuse of ID cards under totalitarian governments such as in South Africa, the former Soviet Union, and China has long been known. Let's consider carefully before we go down that path.

Audio

For iWords and audio passages, go to **SadlierConnect.com**.

Left: A foreign national ID card; Right: fraudulent government documents seized by U.S. Customs in New York

Definitions

Note the spelling, pronunciation, part(s) of speech, and definition(s) of each of the following words. Then write the appropriate form of the word in the blank space in the illustrative sentence(s) following.

1. abject (ab′ jekt)
(*adj.*) degraded; base, contemptible; cringing, servile; complete and unrelieved
In the American dream, those who work hard can escape lives of ____________________ poverty.

2. derelict (der′ ə likt)
(*n.*) someone or something that is abandoned or neglected; (*adj.*) left abandoned; neglectful of duty
The family complained about the unsightly collection of ____________________ cars in its neighbor's driveway.

3. diatribe (dī′ ə trīb)
(*n.*) a bitter and prolonged verbal attack
The senator's speech was more of a ____________________ than a reasoned address.

4. equity (ek′ wət ē)
(*n.*) the state or quality of being just, fair, or impartial; fair and equal treatment; something that is fair; the money value of a property above and beyond any mortgage or other claim
Prompted by considerations of ____________________, the father decided to divide his estate equally among his children.

5. indubitable (in dü′ bə tə bəl)
(*adj.*) certain, not to be doubted or denied
You cannot argue with ____________________ truths.

6. intermittent (in tər mit′ ənt)
(*adj.*) stopping and beginning again, sporadic
She had ____________________ back pains for a week.

7. neophyte (nē′ ə fīt)
(*n.*) a new convert, beginner, novice
In comparison to an experienced wilderness hiker, he is a mere ____________________ in the woods.

8. perspicacity (pər spə kas′ ət ē)
(*n.*) keenness in observing and understanding
The bird watcher scans the surrounding trees and fields with the same ____________________ as a hawk looking for prey.

9. surveillance (sər vāʹ ləns) (*n.*) a watch kept over a person; careful, close, and disciplined observation

The police kept the suspect under strict __________________ after she was released.

10. testy (tesʹ tē) (*adj.*) easily irritated; characterized by impatience and exasperation

The lawyer's __________________ remarks during cross-examination probably affected her credibility with the jury.

Using Context

*For each item, determine whether the **boldface** word from pages 82–83 makes sense in the context of the sentence. Circle the item numbers next to the six sentences in which the words are used correctly.*

1. Rock climbing involves more than physical strength; the climber must observe the rock wall with **perspicacity** and determine the best route to take.
2. After Romeo is banished from Verona, his mother, Lady Montague, descends into a state of **abject** misery and soon dies of grief.
3. The natural history museum is famous for its lifelike **diatribe** that shows models of plants and animals in habitats ranging from deserts to rain forests.
4. The **intermittent** network connection in the hotel where I'm staying makes it difficult for me to email my completed work to the office.
5. The food server's cheerful and **testy** manner garnered him many tips.
6. If you are **derelict** in your responsibility to return those library books, you may be charged a substantial amount in fines.
7. The mountain road became **indubitable** after a tree that had been struck by lightning broke and fell across it.
8. If we want to truly understand what kinds of crops will grow best in these conditions, we will have to consult a **neophyte**.
9. Today many criminals are caught thanks to the constant **surveillance** provided by security cameras in many different locations.
10. The company will study the question of whether there is **equity** in the salaries of its male and female employees.

Choosing the Right Word

*Select the **boldface** word that better completes each sentence. You might refer to the passage on pages 80–81 to see how most of these words are used in context. Note that the choices might be related forms of the Unit words.*

1. Observers on the ground keep close (**surveillance, equity**) on air traffic at a busy airport by means of various electronic devices, such as radar.
2. We laughed at Grandmother's confession that she can be (**testy, abject**) before she has her morning cup of coffee.
3. After over 30 years in Congress, he retains the idealism of the (**diatribe, neophyte**) but has gained the practical wisdom of the veteran.
4. Only an (**intermittent, abject**) coward would stand idly by while a defenseless old woman was mugged in the street.
5. What qualities will he have to fall back on when his (**indubitable, testy**) charm and good looks begin to wear thin?
6. All of a sudden, a strange young man rushed onto the speaker's platform and launched into a(n) (**equity, diatribe**) against "big government."
7. Bag ladies and other homeless (**neophytes, derelicts**) roam our streets in increasing numbers.
8. Today's forecast calls for variable cloudiness with (**testy, intermittent**) periods of rain.
9. The sleeping security guard was (**derelict, indubitable**) in his duties.
10. The historian had long been noted for the soundness of his scholarship and the (**surveillance, perspicacity**) of his judgment.
11. Though I can sometimes be as (**testy, derelict**) as an irate wasp, I normally do not lose my temper very easily.
12. Because she is a fair-minded woman, I'm sure she will present both sides of the controversy with admirable (**equity, perspicacity**).

Completing the Sentence

Choose the word from the word bank that best completes each of the following sentences. Write the correct word or form of the word in the space provided.

abject	**diatribe**	**indubitable**	**neophyte**	**surveillance**
derelict	**equity**	**intermittent**	**perspicacity**	**testy**

1. For years, we carried on a(n) ____________________ correspondence, sometimes allowing months to pass before a letter was answered.

2. I'd say that the phrase "having a short fuse" aptly describes my boss's decidedly ____________________ disposition.

3. How could a mere ____________________ in the teaching profession question the judgment of so experienced an educator?

4. "Simple ____________________ demands that we distribute the tax burden as fairly as possible among the populace," the senator remarked.

5. The ____________________ of her analysis not only clarified the nature of the problem but also suggested its most promising solution.

6. Throughout the period that the spy thought he had gone undetected, he was actually under close ____________________ by the CIA.

7. I would be ____________________ in my duty to you if I did not warn you against the pernicious effects of smoking cigarettes.

8. Every time we did something to anger him, he delivered an intemperate ____________________ lambasting our "hopeless irresponsibility."

9. Though some writers have emphasized Jefferson's human weaknesses, his greatness is also a(n) ____________________ part of the historical record.

10. At the slightest sound of thunder, my dog Rover dives under the bed in a state of ____________________ terror.

End Set A

Definitions

Note the spelling, pronunciation, part(s) of speech, and definition(s) of each of the following words. Then write the appropriate form of the word in the blank space in the illustrative sentence(s) following.

1. agnostic
(ag näs′ tik)

(*n.*) one who believes that nothing can be known about God; a skeptic; (*adj.*) without faith, skeptical

Although he was a confirmed ____________________, he supported the rights of others to practice their religion.

Her ____________________ tendencies made it difficult for her to subscribe to any set of religious beliefs.

2. complicity
(kəm plis′ ə tē)

(*n.*) involvement in wrongdoing; the state of being an accomplice

If you know a crime is going to be committed but do nothing to prevent it, you may be accused of ____________________.

3. effigy
(ef′ ə jē)

(*n.*) a crude image of a despised person

The night before the battle, the troops burned the despised enemy leader in ____________________.

4. inane
(in ān′)

(*adj.*) silly, empty of meaning or value

His ____________________ response left me speechless.

5. indictment
(in dīt′ mənt)

(*n.*) the act of accusing; a formal accusation

The grand jury delivered the ____________________.

6. moot
(müt)

(*adj.*) open to discussion and debate, unresolved; (*v.*) to bring up for discussion; (*n.*) a hypothetical law case argued by students

Whether that was the cause of their troubles is a ____________________ point.

The committee members decided to ____________________ the issue to the full Congress at the earliest opportunity.

The law student prepared for the ____________________.

7. motif
(mō tēf′)

(*n.*) a principal idea, feature, theme, or element; a repeated or dominant figure in a design

The fabric contains an unusual ____________________.

8. plenary
(plēn′ ə rē)

(*adj.*) complete in all aspects or essentials; absolute; attended by all qualified members

Because of its importance, the case was presented at a ____________________ session of the Superior Court.

9. sylvan (sil′ vən)

(*adj.*) pertaining to or characteristic of forests; living or located in a forest; wooded, woody

Once upon a time, Hansel and Gretel walked down a ____________ path, leaving only bread crumbs.

10. travesty (trav′ ə stē)

(*n.*) a grotesque or grossly inferior imitation; a disguise, especially the clothing of the opposite sex; (*v.*) to ridicule by imitating in a broad or burlesque fashion

Instead of modernizing Shakespeare's *Twelfth Night*, they made a ____________ of it.

The new song ____________ the original version.

Using Context

*For each item, determine whether the **boldface** word from pages 86–87 makes sense in the context of the sentence. Circle the item numbers next to the six sentences in which the words are used correctly.*

1. Even if he did not cheat on the test himself, he is guilty of **complicity** for giving the correct answers to his friends.
2. How did we end up having an **inane** conversation about cartoons after hours of intellectual debate?
3. This artist's works are easy to identify because of the floral **motif** that she uses in all of her paintings.
4. He viewed the world from an **agnostic** perspective, believing everyone to be good and worthy of trust.
5. Your **plenary** argument only serves to prove that you are not as well educated in this subject as you claim to be.
6. Some people see the recent extreme weather events as an **indictment** of the human race for disrespecting the planet.
7. How I long to return to that land with its sandy beaches and **sylvan**, open spaces!
8. The much anticipated remake of the beloved classic movie was described as a **travesty** by those who admired the original.
9. The hilltop **effigy**, once the home of a renowned author, is now a museum.
10. The student council argued that some of the school policies were **moot**, but the principal insisted that the rules were not up for discussion.

Choosing the Right Word

*Select the **boldface** word that better completes each sentence. You might refer to the passage on pages 80–81 to see how most of these words are used in context. Note that the choices might be related forms of the Unit words.*

1. Human and animal forms carved in stucco and stone are a common (**motif, travesty**) in ancient Aztec art.
2. Several theology professors have given provocative reviews of the new book by Mr. Stuart, who readily admits he is an (**effigy, agnostic**).
3. The awkward pause in the conversation became even more painful when he interjected his (**plenary, inane**) attempts at humor.
4. His disgraceful behavior since he left college is in itself a(n) (**indictment, complicity**) of the lax, overindulgent upbringing he received.
5. The picture shows the three Graces dancing in a forest clearing, while nymphs, satyrs, and other (**sylvan, agnostic**) creatures cavort among the trees.
6. His extraordinary ability to (**moot, travesty**) the works of popular writers is largely due to his keen eye for the ridiculous.
7. To some readers, the dark and (**inane, sylvan**) setting of Hawthorne's short story "Young Goodman Brown" symbolizes the unknown.
8. Though the book was written by an avowed (**agnostic, motif**), it enjoyed a certain popularity with religious types.
9. "I vetoed that idea when it was first (**mooted, indicted**) years ago," the governor said, "and I have never regretted my decision."
10. As he sat before the fire reading his newspaper, Grandfather seemed the very epitome of (**plenary, sylvan**) contentment.
11. According to that village's custom, one can get rid of an enemy by making a tiny (**effigy, motif**) of him and sticking it full of pins.
12. How can I be accused of (**indictment, complicity**) in that plot when I did not even know the conspirators?

Completing the Sentence

Choose the word from the word bank that best completes each of the following sentences. Write the correct word or form of the word in the space provided.

agnostic	**effigy**	**indictment**	**motif**	**sylvan**
complicity	**inane**	**moot**	**plenary**	**travesty**

1. It was such a(n) ____________________ remark that I couldn't keep myself from laughing derisively when I heard it.

2. Since he neither affirms nor denies the existence of God, I'd classify him as a(n) ____________________ rather than an atheist.

3. The fact that so many released prisoners return to a life of crime is in itself a terrifying ____________________ of our penal system.

4. Those who saw the young woman being assaulted and did nothing to help her were guilty of ____________________ in the crime.

5. Since the accused was never really given a chance to defend himself, his so-called trial was nothing but a(n) ____________________ of justice.

6. In Wagner's operas, brief musical ____________________ associated with the characters or their actions recur again and again.

7. In her garland of leaves and acorns, the child looked very much like some ____________________ spirit from an Arthurian myth.

8. How can you call that a(n) ____________________ question when it is quite clearly a simple matter of right and wrong?

9. During the emergency, the mayor assumed ____________________ authority and did whatever was needed to provide essential services.

10. The overthrown dictator was hanged in ____________________ before a vast throng in the town square.

End Set B

Synonyms

*Choose the word or form of the word from this Unit that is the same or most nearly the same in meaning as the **boldface** word or expression in the phrase. Write that word on the line. Use a dictionary if necessary.*

1. **remiss** in discharging her responsibilities ____________
2. a crude **likeness** ____________
3. admired for his uncommon **acuity** ____________
4. **fitful** bursts of energy ____________
5. a questioning **nonbeliever** ____________
6. the **vapid** chatter of thoughtless critics ____________
7. a flower **pattern** ____________
8. the **charge** against the burglar ____________
9. a **parody** of Dickens's work ____________
10. the **forested** slopes of the Rockies ____________
11. a **tirade** against the proposed law ____________
12. was given **unlimited** power to govern ____________
13. their level of **involvement** ____________
14. put under **scrutiny** ____________
15. indoctrinated the **rookie** ____________

Antonyms

*Choose the word or form of the word from this Unit that is most nearly opposite in meaning to the **boldface** word or expression in the phrase. Write that word on the line. Use a dictionary if necessary.*

1. offered a **high-handed** apology ____________
2. considered both sides with **prejudice** ____________
3. an **imperturbable** demeanor ____________
4. of **dubious** character ____________
5. an **indisputable** point ____________

Writing: Words in Action

Think about the arguments offered by each side in the debate. Do you believe every U.S. citizen should be required to have a national identity card? Write a persuasive essay that supports your position on this issue. Use at least two details from the passage (pages 80–81) and three or more words from this Unit.

Vocabulary in Context

Some of the words you have studied in this Unit appear in ***boldface*** *type. Read the passage below, and then circle the letter of the correct answer for each word as it is used in context.*

Perhaps the earliest record of a passport-like document is in the Bible's Book of Nehemiah, which has the royal cup-bearer getting a letter from his king requesting that governors beyond the Euphrates River give him "safe passage." This remains the **motif** of passports to the present day. Bearers are granted safe conduct while visiting foreign lands. As Nehemiah's "passport" demonstrates, the document had distinctly aristocratic origins. Kings and queens provided the letters to their ministers, wealthy merchants, and favored subjects, allowing the bearers to travel safely from **sylvan** Norway to arid Morocco. Whether the letters became known as "passports" because travelers passed through ports or because they entered city gates ("portes" in French) is a subject of debate.

By the nineteenth century, most European countries had begun issuing passports on a more general basis. But the surge in rail travel in the latter part of the century swamped passport bureaucracies, and the document gradually fell out of use. The outbreak of World War I quickly brought it back. The possibility of spies crossing international boundaries unnoticed led to the first standardized passport, complete with a signature, physical description, and primitive photograph—a near **effigy** of the unfortunate bearer. Ever since the Great War, control and **surveillance** have been major factors in the development of passport regulations.

Fortunately, along with stricter passport standards, most nations have also striven to make passports fairer and more democratic. **Equity** demands that passports be available—and affordable—to all citizens with a desire or need to travel. So passport applications are relatively simple and cheap, making it difficult to be **agnostic** about the value of a passport.

---

1. A **motif** is a(n)
a. principal idea
b. implied meaning
c. background
d. explanation

2. A **sylvan** nation, as Norway is said to be, is
a. wild
b. northern
c. snowy
d. forested

3. An **effigy** is
a. a printed copy
b. a crude image
c. a reproduction
d. a photographic negative

4. **Surveillance** requires careful
a. mapping
b. observation
c. war planning
d. documentation

5. The word **equity** most nearly means
a. equivalence
b. compassion
c. economical
d. fairness

6. A person who is **agnostic** is
a. official
b. political
c. skeptical
d. susceptible

Vocabulary for Comprehension

Part 1

*Read this passage, which contains words in **boldface** that appear in Units 4–6. Then choose the best answer to each question based on what is stated or implied in the passage. You may refer to the passage as often as necessary.*

Questions 1–10 are based on the following passage.

It is proverbially difficult to delineate the origins of historic movements, and jazz is no exception. Even to define this uniquely American musical style is challenging. Since it emerged around the turn of the twentieth century, jazz has been evolving.

What can be confidently asserted is that jazz **garnered** its original shape from a fusion of European and West African sources and styles. The rhythmic and structural features of jazz derive mostly from West African traditions. The same is true for some of the instrumentation in jazz with the frequent use of banjo and percussion. Most instrumentation in jazz, however, as well as its harmonic structure, developed from European influences; as seen in the use of the trumpet, trombone, string bass, and piano.

Just as jazz fuses the traditions of two continents, this style has lingered for most of its history midway between extemporized improvisation and fixed composition. Another distinguishing characteristic of jazz is that the jazz performer takes precedence over the composer. In fact, it is fair to conclude that the creative, improvising performer *is* the composer. In classical music, on the other hand, the performer interprets another individual's composition. There are exceptions: one thinks of Wolfgang Amadeus Mozart, who managed as a child prodigy to fuse composition, improvisation, and performance.

Rhythmic syncopation has long been **reputed** to be integral to jazz, but this tenet, as often with analysis of the style, has sometimes been dismissed as **sophistry**. In syncopation, the weak beat in a phrase is stressed, not the strong beat, resulting in a brief displacement. This **idiosyncrasy** exists in classical music as far back as Bach and Handel in the eighteenth century, and syncopation was a prominent feature in ragtime, one of jazz's immediate American precursors. Syncopation was often deemed essential to "swing," the New Orleans style that dominated the early years of jazz. Yet trumpeters Louis Armstrong and Bunny Berigan roundly disproved this notion by repeating unsyncopated quarter notes that generated **consummate** swing.

By 1918, jazz was firmly established in New Orleans. It spread rapidly from this **bastion** to other cities, including Kansas City, Memphis, Denver, Chicago, and New York. By 1922, the writer F. Scott Fitzgerald, whose fiction brilliantly reflected the mood and tone of the "Roaring Twenties," had coined the term "the Jazz Age." Flappers with bobbed hair typified the era, and **frenetic** dances like the Charleston and the lindy hop became the **ubiquitous** pulse of entertainment. African American culture flourished in the Harlem Renaissance, and jazz had a **fecund** impact on the visual and performing arts with the work of Archibald Motley, Romare Bearden, and Stuart Davis.

Among the numerous complex, enigmatic features of the nature and development of jazz as a musical style, experts continue to puzzle over the question of American uniqueness. Why did jazz not develop in the Caribbean or in South America, despite the presence of thousands of people with African origins in those regions? Music historians theorize that emancipation in such areas may have resulted in inhibiting fusion, since people were able to retain their traditions in a relatively pure form.

1. The primary purpose of the passage is to
A) survey the origins and features of jazz.
B) refute the notion that jazz has remained a monolithic, unchanging musical style.
C) describe jazz's international impact.
D) explain how jazz utilized European musical forms and traditions

2. The author suggests that jazz's harmonic structure may be traced to
A) European influences.
B) ragtime and blues.
C) West African influences.
D) early jazz performers in New Orleans.

3. Which choice provides the best evidence for the answer to the previous question?
A) Lines 7–10 ("What can . . . styles")
B) Lines 10–12 ("rhythmic . . . traditions")
C) Lines 12–15 ("The . . . percussion")
D) Lines 15–19 ("Most. . . piano")

4. As it is used in line 8, "garnered" most nearly means
A) dissipated.
B) acquired.
C) culled.
D) sowed.

5. The overall purpose of lines 24–29 is to
A) discuss the role of improvisation and the performer in jazz.
B) compare and contrast Mozart with the typical jazz performer.
C) refute the theory that improvisation is integral to jazz compositions.
D) assert that jazz performers must improvise in order to be truly creative.

6. As it is used in line 40, "sophistry" most nearly means
A) pretension.
B) fallacy.
C) ribaldry.
D) hyperbole.

7. What point is the author making by including the fourth paragraph (lines 36–54)?
A) Ragtime stresses the weak beat.
B) Swing music was a precursor to jazz.
C) Syncopation is used in, but not integral to, jazz music.
D) Syncopation is used in classical music.

8. What is the main idea of the fifth paragraph (lines 55–70)?
A) The influence of jazz music spread all over the country and to other art forms.
B) Stuart Davis's art is an example of jazz music's influence on painting.
C) F. Scott Fitzgerald started "the Jazz Age."
D) Archibald Motley was influenced by jazz.

9. As it is used in line 68, "fecund" most nearly means
A) fruitful.
B) barren.
C) plenteous.
D) radiant.

10. In the last paragraph, it can most reasonably be inferred that the most likely reason for the failure of jazz to take root in the Caribbean and South America was that
A) these regions already possessed distinctive indigenous styles of music.
B) poor communications hampered the diffusion of innovative styles.
C) traditions in these countries were not heavily influenced by other cultures.
D) these areas were relatively devoid of exposure to foreign music.

Vocabulary for Comprehension

Part 2

*Read these passages, which contain words in **boldface** that appear in Units 4–6. Then choose the best answer to each question based on what is stated or implied in the passage(s). You may refer to the passages as often as necessary.*

Questions 1–10 are based on the following passages.

Passage 1

Philosophy has been defined as the critical examination of the grounds for fundamental beliefs. In western philosophy, the ancient Greek philosopher Socrates (c.469–399 BCE) is regarded as the fountainhead, though it is difficult to **delineate** the difference between Socratic doctrines and those of his disciple, Plato.

Socrates was a moral philosopher, pondering the question of how human beings should live their lives. He said "The unexamined life is not worth living." Socrates is known for intellectual brilliance and personal eccentricity, challenging his interlocutors to define virtues such as piety, courage, and justice. His technique of question-and-answer, subsequently known as the "Socratic method," became an educational keystone.

Late fifth-century Athens existed on the cusp of numerous seismic shifts, and the Athenians were in transition from an oral to a written culture. Socrates firmly resisted writing as a vehicle for philosophy, holding instead that dialectic, or verbal give-and-take, was far superior to the written word. Writing, he believed, invited ideas to **atrophy.** Ironically, we know of Socrates's teachings primarily through Plato, who immortalized his teacher in writing. In ethics, Socrates was a nonconformist. In defiance of traditional Greek beliefs, he **mooted** the notion that it was better to suffer an injury than to inflict one, since wrongdoing harmed the soul.

In 399 BCE, in the wake of the Athenians' defeat in the Peloponnesian War, a group of **nettled** opponents accused Socrates of impiety and corrupting the city's youth; **incarcerated,** he died in **ignominy**.

Passage 2

Philosophy translates as "love of wisdom." The study of philosophy is the study of fundamental beliefs and universal problems that influence how members of society think and live.

The earliest written Western philosophers were the Greeks. Aristotle was a student of Plato, himself a student of Socrates. In the year 367 BCE, Aristotle began as a **neophyte** at the Athenian Academy and studied there for twenty years.

In the year 335 BCE Aristotle opened his Lyceum, a school for advanced study. Aristotle created a large body of written work showing his wide-ranging interests, including biology and history. The human quest for truth, Aristotle contended, comes from the need to understand and to find answers to things we do not understand. Only thirty-one of the hundreds of texts he wrote survived, and he describes different bodies of study, **motifs** that we recognize today: theoretical sciences (philosophy, mathematics, physics), practical sciences (politics and ethics) and productive sciences (farming, medicine, the arts, and woodworking). One thread winds through all of the sciences and that is logic, or correct reasoning. Logic and inquiry are the foundations of all areas of study. In embracing a method of observation and reasoning to **glean** an understanding the world, he stood in contrast with the earlier teachings of Plato and Socrates, whose studies of ethics and question-and-answer methods fostered a theoretical approach to understanding the world.

1. As it is used in line 7, "delineate" most nearly means
A) describe.
B) belittle.
C) jostle.
D) embrace.

2. In Passage 1, the "Socratic method" (line 18) consists of
A) question and answer.
B) problem and solution.
C) comparison and contrast.
D) thesis, antithesis, and synthesis.

3. As it is used in line 33, "mooted" most nearly means
A) recapitulated.
B) undermined.
C) debated.
D) broached.

4. As it is used in line 50, "neophyte'" most nearly means
A) professional.
B) beginner.
C) convert.
D) participant.

5. It can reasonably be inferred from Passage 2, lines 61–67, that
A) Aristotle used question-and-answer as a basis for his logic.
B) scholars are still searching for the missing texts of Aristotle.
C) scholars still study the sciences described by Aristotle.
D) the scope of Aristotle's teaching will never be known.

6. As it is used in line 62, "motifs" most nearly means
A) themes.
B) patterns.
C) fragments.
D) refrains.

7. According to both passages, what is one way Aristotle differed from Socrates?
A) Aristotle studied the military policy and the performing arts, while Socrates did not.
B) Aristotle believed in the military, while Socrates believed "it was better to suffer an injury than to inflict one."
C) Aristotle created a large body of written work, while Socrates believed to write thoughts down was to kill their growth.
D) Aristotle believed in learning through discussion; Socrates favored experience.

8. In Passage 1, Socrates is described as a moral philosopher, concerned with ideas, and in Passage 2, Aristotle is described as
A) building on Socrates's ideas.
B) uninterested in questions of morality.
C) adhering to the teachings of his predecessor, Plato.
D) studying the physical world through observation.

9. Which choice provides the best evidence for the answer to the previous question?
A) Lines 41–45 ("Philosophy ... live")
B) Lines 46–48 ("The earliest ... Socrates")
C) Lines 67–70 ("One thread ... study")
D) Lines 70–77 ("In ... world")

10. Which statement best describes the overall relationship between Passage 1 and Passage 2?
A) Passage 1 discusses a stereotype; Passage 2 has biographical details.
B) Only Passage 2 cites the impact of a philosopher on his contemporaries.
C) Both passages survey the life and achievements of their subjects.
D) Both passages emphasize questions that the philosophers left unanswered.

Synonyms

*From the word bank below, choose the word that has the same or nearly the same meaning as the **boldface** word in each sentence and write it on the line. You will not use all of the words.*

agnostic	**effigy**	**inane**	**nuance**
concord	**esoteric**	**motif**	**pusillanimous**
depraved	**glean**	**mundane**	**reputed**
diatribe	**idiosyncrasy**	**neophyte**	**sophistry**

1. She hoped that she could spend her day off doing something fun, but instead it was full of **humdrum** errands. ____________________

2. His mispronunciation could be a **quirk** of his regional dialect, but I suspect he doesn't know he is saying anything incorrectly. ____________________

3. I tried to **cull** information about the author's private life by reading some of her published personal letters, but nothing hinted at anything besides her career. ____________________

4. My tidy roommate gets so upset if anyone moves his things that he will deliver a **tirade** about how disrespectful it is. ____________________

5. The conversation about the reality television show was **moronic**, so I began to tune it out. ____________________

6. The two friends developed a **cryptic** code so that if their notes were ever intercepted, the messages would seem completely innocent. ____________________

7. This sequel gives audiences a glimpse into the early life of the villain and the malevolent influences for such **corrupt** behavior. ____________________

8. Everyone was surprised when our manager, the **widely accepted** next-in-command for the executive position, did not get the job. ____________________

9. Mocking people who audition for this play while being too scared to do it yourself shows just how **lily-livered** you are! ____________________

10. Unlike many siblings, the twins live in a near-constant state of **harmony** and rarely ever fight. ____________________

11. After going weeks without practicing, she felt like a **beginner** as she cautiously raised the violin to her shoulder. ____________________

12. Even though I consider myself a **doubter**, I am still curious about the history and customs of all religions. ____________________

Two-Word Completions

Select the pair of words that best completes the meaning of each of the following sentences.

1. Edward R. Murrow will hold a place in history as a journalist who saw in 1950s television the potential to educate, and not simply to entertain. He felt it was the ________________ responsibility of all journalists to act as a(n) ________________ against both zealotry and indifference.

a. incumbent ... bastion
b. overweening ... indictment
c. plenary ... grouse
d. consummate ... fiat

2. The wealthy widow had a(n) ________________ for fine clothes and ________________ meals.

a. acuity ... recumbent
b. stratagem ... pecuniary
c. penchant ... sumptuous
d. flotsam ... fecund

3. I'm extremely circumspect about what I say or do in the office because my boss is so ________________ that it is easy to ________________ or exasperate him.

a. abject ... moot
b. mordant ... disarray
c. jocular ... enervate
d. testy ... nettle

4. After the battle, the officer who had failed to carry out his orders was arrested by the military police, charged with ________________ of duty, and ________________ in the stockade, pending a court-martial.

a. dereliction ... incarcerated
b. ignominy ... hallowed
c. atrophy ... garnered
d. travesty ... mooted

5. Despite the harried officer's ________________ attempts to steady his troops after the left flank had been turned, they fled from the field in such ________________ that their departure was more of a rout than a retreat.

a. intermittent ... concord
b. frenetic ... disarray
c. consummate ... ignominy
d. ludicrous ... equity

6. Vincent van Gogh was indeed a(n) ________________ technician, able to ________________ every nuance of nature's variegated panorama with a mere stroke of the brush.

a. consummate ... delineate
b. indubitable ... enervate
c. sylvan ... travesty
d. ubiquitous ... hallow

7. Although the man is certainly thought to have been involved in the crime, no ________________ has yet been brought against him because the authorities have not been able to assemble enough evidence to establish his ________________ beyond a reasonable doubt.

a. exigency ... acuity
b. figment ... perspicacity
c. indictment ... complicity
d. surveillance ... equity

Denotation and Connotation

The **denotation** of a word—its definition—is objective. It can be found in the dictionary. Many words, however, have one or more subjective meanings. They are the emotional associations, or **connotations**, of a word. Connotations can be positive or negative.

Connotations create and convey a precise mood or message. For instance, to convey not only intelligence but also suggest a lack of candor, a writer might instead describe the characters as *cunning, sly,* or *wily.*

Consider these synonyms for the neutral word *intermittent*:

sporadic *variable* *desultory* *spasmodic*

Sporadic and *variable* have neutral or positive connotations, describing something occurring at irregular intervals. The negative connotations of *desultory* and *spasmodic* suggest that the lack of regularity is unfortunate, disappointing, or even violent.

Look at these examples of words that are similar in denotation but have different connotations.

NEUTRAL	POSITIVE	NEGATIVE
utterance	**tribute**	**diatribe**
timid	**retiring**	**pusillanimous**
reasoning	**sagacity**	**sophistry**

Expressing the Connotation

Read each sentence. Select the word in parentheses that expresses the connotation (positive, negative, or neutral) given at the beginning of the sentence.

negative **1.** The girl is planning to (**imitate, travesty**) Shakespeare's sonnet by rewriting it as a limerick.

positive **2.** Sean's (**whimsical, inane**) comments made me appreciate his unique wit.

neutral **3.** The hotel staff worked at a (**frenetic, bustling**) pace as the wedding guests began to arrive.

neutral **4.** One (**idiosyncrasy, flaw**) of William Faulkner's writing style is his use of long sentences with multiple independent and dependent clauses.

neutral **5.** The newspaper report hinted at the elderly woman's (**participation, complicity**) in the recent police investigation.

positive **6.** In last Sunday's recital, the cellist's (**terminal, consummate**) performance of a Beethoven concerto surprised the audience.

positive **7.** The chaperone was pleased by the cooperation and (**demeanor, concord**) her young students displayed on the field trip.

negative **8.** As they spilled into the streets, angry protestors displayed (**effigies, embodiments**) of the tyrannical dictator.

Classical Roots

gno(s)—to know

The Greek root *gno(s)* appears in **agnostic** (page 86). The literal meaning is "one who does not know." In modern usage the word refers to an individual who believes that nothing can be known about God, or a skeptic.

cognate	**cognizant**	**gnostic**	**prognosis**
cognition	**diagnose**	**ignore**	**recognize**

From the list of words above, choose the one that corresponds to each of the brief definitions below. Write the word in the blank space in the illustrative sentence below the definition. Use an online or print dictionary if necessary.

1. of, relating to, or possessing intellectual or spiritual knowledge
Many religions observe a ____________________ doctrine, where emphasis is placed on the pursuit of spiritual and intellectual knowledge.

2. a prediction of the probable course of a disease; a probable forecast or estimate
With modern treatment options, patients who contract this once-fatal disease now have an excellent ____________________ for full recovery.

3. fully informed; conscious; aware
As a result of a 1966 court decision, all arrested suspects must be made ____________________ of their Miranda rights.

4. to identify a disease or condition based on observation, examination, and analysis
A podiatrist is trained to ____________________ and treat a range of problems of the foot.

5. to know, identify, or show awareness of something from past experience or knowledge; to accept as a fact; to acknowledge a thing's existence, validity, or authority; to approve of or appreciate
The school board has come to ____________________ the positive impact of art and music classes.

6. related by family or origin; related in nature, character, quality, or function; a person or thing related to another
The Sanskrit word for king—*rajah*—is a ____________________ of the Latin *rex*.

7. the broad mental process by which knowledge is acquired, including aspects of awareness, perception, reasoning, judgment, memory, and intuition; knowledge
After a serious blow to the head, her ____________________ was impaired for several weeks.

8. to disregard deliberately; to pay no attention to; to refuse to consider
If we just ____________________ Rover, he will eventually stop begging for food at the table.

UNIT 7

Read the following passage, taking note of the **boldface** *words and their contexts. These words are among those you will be studying in Unit 7. It may help you to complete the exercises in this Unit if you refer to the way the words are used below.*

John Lennon's Legacy

<Biographical Sketch>

John Lennon was born in Liverpool, England, on October 9, 1940, at the height of World War II. Forty years later, on December 8, 1980, he was shot dead by a mentally unstable fan outside his Manhattan apartment. During his short life, as a musician, artist, poet, and political activist, Lennon transcended his time. "If someone thinks that love and peace is a cliché that must have been left behind in the '60s, that's his problem," he said. "Love and peace are eternal."

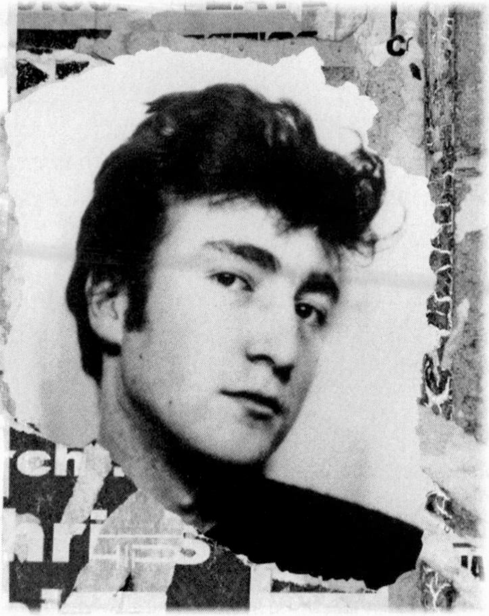

John Lennon in 1961

Lennon's father left his wife and young son before World War II ended. Poor but never **indigent**, Lennon's mother, Julia, entrusted the boy to her sister, Mimi, one of a **coterie** of "five strong, intelligent sisters," as Lennon later recalled. During his childhood, Lennon spent an **inordinate** amount of time with **convivial** female relatives. In later years, he said that this was his "first feminist education" and that living apart from his parents enabled him "to see that parents are not gods" but were human and had flaws just like everyone else.

Despite their living apart, Julia Lennon maintained a close relationship with her son. She encouraged his interest in music, rather than demand that he **jettison** his musical aspirations (as his Aunt Mimi hoped he would do), even giving him his first guitar when he was fifteen. The gift was **felicitous**, as Lennon dove into music with **pertinacious** ambition. His belief that it would bring him lasting fame was as strong as Aunt Mimi's conviction that his hopes were **illusory**.

Lennon soon realized his dream of fame, thanks to the success of the Beatles, the band he formed with his songwriting **counterpart**, Paul McCartney. The band rocketed to fame in the early 1960s, propelled by energetic pop songs like "Love Me Do," simple variations on the time-honored theme of teenage love.

With age comes wisdom. As Lennon's artistic vision matured, he led the Beatles toward new horizons, and his lyrics increasingly contained intricate metaphors and political themes. Lennon's humor, free spirit, and politics soon permeated the band's image and music, a transformation marked by the album *Sgt. Pepper's Lonely Hearts Club Band.* The album cover ridicules military formality, presenting the bandmates in **garish** uniforms, **raiment** that was absurd even for its era. Lennon's maturing talents shine in songs like "A Day in the Life," which weaves themes of class and political power with images of mundane and tragic moments in life; the lyrics are a dreamlike tapestry **embellished** with metaphor. Critics soon acknowledged Lennon as a worthy modern poet.

The Beatles in the BBC's *Top of the Pops* television show in June 1966

John Lennon and Yoko Ono, his wife, in a war protest, London, 1969

Politics and poetry remained at the fore of Lennon's songwriting as he became a high-profile social activist. U.S. leaders, mired in the Vietnam War, objected to the **effrontery** of this popular British "peacenik" and had him monitored by the FBI, which diligently collected **picayune** details for his file. Lennon did little to **allay** their concerns. Many of his lyrics, such as those in "All You Need Is Love" and, later, "Imagine," rallied those who **demurred** violence. As a group, the Beatles proved more **ephemeral** than their fame, and personal tensions broke up the band. Yet Lennon continued to speak passionately against violence and enmity with solo works like "Give Peace a Chance."

"We're not being unreasonable. Just saying 'give it a chance,'" said Lennon in 1980 when discussing his desire for a world without war. With "Imagine," he was asking for a world without hate, greed, or hunger. "It's the same message over and over. And it's positive," he said of his work. Lennon's devotion to such positive messages, his willingness to use his art and fame to promote love and peace among all people, is his most enduring legacy.

Audio

For iWords and audio passages, go to **SadlierConnect.com**.

Definitions

Note the spelling, pronunciation, part(s) of speech, and definition(s) of each of the following words. Then write the appropriate form of the word in the blank space in the illustrative sentence(s) following.

1. convivial (kən viv′ ē əl)
(*adj.*) festive, sociable, having fun together, genial
Thanksgiving dinner at Grandmother's house is always a ____________________ family gathering.

2. coterie (kō′ tə rē)
(*n.*) a circle of acquaintances; a close-knit, often exclusive, group of people with a common interest
Robert Browning and his ____________________ had ideas about poetry that seemed revolutionary in their day.

3. demur (di mər′)
(*v.*) to object or take exception to; (*n.*) an objection
The rank and file will ____________________ if they are not consulted regularly by the union leadership.
The speech in favor of the proposal was drowned out by a chorus of ____________________ from the senate floor.

4. embellish (em bel′ ish)
(*v.*) to decorate, adorn, touch up; to improve by adding details
The best storytellers ____________________ their tales in ways that help readers visualize the setting.

5. felicitous (fə lis′ ə təs)
(*adj.*) appropriate, apt, well chosen; marked by well-being or good fortune, happy
In view of the high prices for home heating oil, the mild winter was a ____________________ turn of events.

6. illusory (i lü′ sə rē)
(*adj.*) misleading, deceptive; lacking in or not based on reality
Police state tactics provide an ____________________ sense of security in an unjust society.

7. indigent (in′ də jənt)
(*adj.*) needy, impoverished
The number of homeless and ____________________ persons has increased since the economy took a downturn.

8. misanthrope (mis′ ən thrōp)
(*n.*) a person who hates or despises people
The millionaire ____________________ left all her money to an animal shelter and not a penny to a single human being.

9. pertinacious (pər tə nā′ shəs) (*adj.*) very persistent; holding firmly to a course of action or a set of beliefs; hard to get rid of, refusing to be put off or denied

The defense attorney was as ____________________ as a bulldog in his cross-examination of the witness.

10. picayune (pik ē yün′) (*adj.*) of little value or importance, paltry, measly; concerned with trifling matters, small-minded

A supervisor who fusses about every ____________________ fault of the workers will lower morale and productivity.

Using Context

*For each item, determine whether the **boldface** word from pages 102–103 makes sense in the context of the sentence. Circle the item numbers next to the six sentences in which the words are used correctly.*

1. For me, simply wrapping a gift is not enough; I like to **embellish** the parcel with bows, ribbons, and a small trinket.

2. In Mark Twain's *The Prince and the Pauper*, the young Prince of Wales poses as a beggar and lives for a time among some **indigent** Londoners.

3. The houses damaged in the flood will not be **convivial** for months because major repairs are needed.

4. Are their hopes of breaking the world record **illusory**, or do they have a realistic chance of doing so?

5. The Bloomsbury Group was a **coterie** of artists and writers that included novelists Virginia Woolf and E. M. Forster.

6. Critics praised the writer's stories for the thoroughly true-to-life characters and compelling, **picayune** details.

7. Their meeting at the piano competition turned out to be a **felicitous** event, since two years later they were happily married and proudly expecting twins.

8. After her death, many people honored the **misanthrope** for her generosity and benevolence in the community.

9. The inexperienced worker decided to **demur** to his supervisor for advice on the mishap.

10. Despite economic challenges and physical setbacks, the **pertinacious** young gymnast would not give up on her ambition of competing in the Olympics.

Choosing the Right Word

*Select the **boldface** word that better completes each sentence. You might refer to the passage on pages 100–101 to see how most of these words are used in context. Note that the choices might be related forms of the Unit words.*

1. Ralph Waldo Emerson and a (**coterie, demur**) of like-minded friends led the American transcendentalism movement in the mid-nineteenth century.

2. To celebrate their fiftieth anniversary, my grandfather described the (**felicitous, indigent**) choice he made to ask my grandmother for a first date.

3. She has neither the starry-eyed optimism of the idealist nor the mordant cynicism of the (**misanthrope, coterie**).

4. I am flattered that you want me to chair the meeting, but I must (**demur, embellish**) on the grounds of my youth and inexperience.

5. If installment buying is not carefully controlled, the benefits that can accrue from it may prove wholly (**illusory, pertinacious**).

6. I can always come up with the crushing rejoinder, the dazzling witticism, or the (**picayune, felicitous**) phrase—about an hour after I need it!

7. The famous sleuth pursued his investigation with all the (**pertinacity, conviviality**) of a lion stalking its dinner.

8. As the rock star's popularity began to skyrocket, what had been a small (**coterie, misanthrope**) of admirers became an unruly mob.

9. Though the federal government does much to help the (**indigent, illusory**), private charities play no small part in their welfare.

10. The proofreader didn't notice any significant flaws in the writing, but she did find a few (**felicitous, picayune**) errors in the punctuation.

11. To anyone as fond of horses as I am, the stable and the tack room provide as (**indigent, convivial**) an atmosphere as one could wish for.

12. When the facts of a matter speak so plainly for themselves, we shouldn't seek to (**embellish, demur**) them.

Completing the Sentence

Choose the word from the word bank that best completes each of the following sentences. Write the correct word or form of the word in the space provided.

convivial	**demur**	**felicitous**	**indigent**	**pertinacious**
coterie	**embellish**	**illusory**	**misanthrope**	**picayune**

1. Jonathan Swift so came to loathe human folly, vice, and hypocrisy that he died a virtual ____________________.

2. Who wouldn't have had fun among such a(n) ____________________ group of people?

3. In the Victorian era, designers ____________________ women's dresses with all sorts of elaborate frills and flounces.

4. Since we all agreed that the proposal seemed to offer the best solution to our problem, it was accepted without ____________________.

5. The disastrous stock market crash of 1929 left many a wealthy speculator as ____________________ as the proverbial church mouse.

6. "If at first you don't succeed, try, try again" seems to be the motto of that ____________________ young woman.

7. The "Old 400" was a very small and exclusive ____________________ of prominent families that dominated East Coast society for decades.

8. A busy administrator in today's high-pressure business world just doesn't have time to deal with such ____________________ concerns as making coffee.

9. A good deal of sad experience has taught me that my youthful hopes of getting something for nothing are entirely ____________________.

10. Though I don't consider myself much of a diplomat, I think I handled that delicate situation in a particularly ____________________ manner.

End Set A

Definitions

Note the spelling, pronunciation, part(s) of speech, and definition(s) of each of the following words. Then write the appropriate form of the word in the blank space in the illustrative sentence(s) following.

1. allay (ə lā′)
(*v.*) to calm or pacify, set to rest; to lessen or relieve
The politician made a speech in order to ____________ his constituents' fears.

2. bestial (bes′ chəl)
(*adj.*) beastlike; beastly, brutal; subhuman in intelligence and sensibility
In beating their prisoner, the guards were guilty of a truly ____________ act.

3. counterpart (kau̇nt′ ər pärt)
(*n.*) a person or thing closely resembling or corresponding to another; a complement
I have to admit I was frightened of my ____________ on the other team because she held the high-jump record.

4. effrontery (ə frən′ tə rē)
(*n.*) shameless boldness, impudence
After having been suspended for disrespectful behavior, the student had the ____________ to talk back to his teacher again.

5. ephemeral (i fem′ ər əl)
(*adj.*) lasting only a short time, short-lived
Only the greatest of writers and artists achieve anything other than ____________ popularity.

6. furtive (fər′ tiv)
(*adj.*) done slyly or stealthily, sneaky, secret, shifty; stolen
The girl was caught taking a ____________ glance at the test paper of the student sitting next to her.

7. garish (gar′ ish)
(*adj.*) glaring; tastelessly showy or overdecorated in a vulgar or offensive way
The storefront was painted in ____________ colors so that it would attract the attention of passersby.

8. inordinate (in ôr′ də nət)
(*adj.*) far too great, exceeding reasonable limits, excessive
The press showered the popular actor with ____________ praise for what seemed a rather ordinary performance.

9. jettison (jet′ ə sən) — (*v.*) to cast overboard, get rid of as unnecessary or burdensome

The captain ordered the crew to ____________ the ballast so the ship could move more quickly through the water.

10. raiment (rā′ mənt) — (*n.*) clothing, garments

When the chorus in the Greek tragedy hears that the king has died, they tear their ____________ in anguish.

Using Context

*For each item, determine whether the **boldface** word from pages 106–107 makes sense in the context of the sentence. Circle the item numbers next to the six sentences in which the words are used correctly.*

1. I admire his ability to treat everyone in the office, from the president to the custodial staff, with the greatest **effrontery**.

2. We spent such an **inordinate** amount of time deciding on our team name that we had only a few minutes left to discuss our strategy before the competition.

3. Will her desire to learn the piano last, or will it be just another one of her **ephemeral** interests?

4. The columnist answered questions about etiquette, manners, and the appropriate **bestial** behavior for specific situations.

5. The realtor told the homeowners they could attract more buyers if they refurbished their foyer, which assailed visitors with clashing colors and **garish** décor.

6. As the last **raiment** of light from the sun cast its hue across the waters, we set sail for home.

7. When the director announced that I had the lead role in the school musical, I snuck a **furtive** glance at my friend, who had auditioned for the same role, to see if he seemed disappointed.

8. The manager's repeated pledges that everyone's job was safe did not **allay** employees' fears about potential layoffs; it only worried the workers more.

9. I hoped to **jettison** the process of my family's departure to the airport by printing everyone's boarding passes, but we still ended up delayed because my father misplaced his passport.

10. Before the match began, our team captain shook hands with her **counterpart** from the other school as a sign of sportsmanship.

Set B

Choosing the Right Word

*Select the **boldface** word that better completes each sentence. You might refer to the passage on pages 100–101 to see how most of these words are used in context. Note that the choices might be related forms of the Unit words.*

1. The kind of (**garish, ephemeral**) theatrical makeup used by circus clowns is not suitable for an elegant fashion model.
2. Somehow, it depresses me to think that with the approach of winter this magnificent old tree will surrender all its leafy (**raiment, counterpart**).
3. Nothing we could say seemed to (**jettison, allay**) her grief over the loss of her dog.
4. When I returned to the office earlier than expected, I caught the little snoop (**inordinately, furtively**) going through the papers on my desk.
5. The atrocities committed by the (**garish, bestial**) commanders of such concentration camps as Auschwitz appalled the civilized world.
6. Sadly, in our celebrity-obsessed culture, professional athletes make (**furtive, inordinate**) amounts of money while professional educators make little.
7. "You mean you had the (**effrontery, raiment**) to ask for a raise when everyone knows you've been goofing off lately?" I asked in amazement.
8. Not surprisingly, my sister's solemnly made commitment to daily clarinet practice for one month was (**inordinate, ephemeral**), lasting only five days.
9. Every dynamic and successful society must be able to (**allay, jettison**) ideas and institutions that have outlived their usefulness.
10. An emotion so fickle and (**ephemeral, bestial**) does not deserve to be categorized as "love."
11. Often the antonym of a given English word is not so much its opposite as its (**effrontery, counterpart**)—for example, *actor* and *actress*.
12. The presidency is the "toughest job in the world" because it makes such (**bestial, inordinate**) demands on a person's time, energy, and ingenuity.

Completing the Sentence

Choose the word from the word bank that best completes each of the following sentences. Write the correct word or form of the word in the space provided.

allay	**counterpart**	**ephemeral**	**garish**	**jettison**
bestial	**effrontery**	**furtive**	**inordinate**	**raiment**

1. The man's features suddenly contorted into a(n) ____________________ mask, more reminiscent of a hobgoblin than a human being.

2. The ____________________ movie palaces of an earlier era have given way to smaller theaters, decorated in a simpler, more austere style.

3. The ____________________ manner in which she sidled into the room and tried to avoid being noticed actually drew attention to her presence.

4. The crew of the freighter ____________________ most of its cargo in a desperate effort to keep the sinking ship afloat.

5. She had the ____________________ to come into my own home to tell me what I should do to help her.

6. She is entitled to reasonable compensation for the damage to her car, but the demands she has made are totally ____________________.

7. Recent developments in that part of the world have intensified rather than ____________________ our fears of a renewed conflict.

8. At the Casablanca Conference in 1943, President Roosevelt and his military aides met with their British ____________________ to map military strategy for the Western Allies.

9. When Charles V retired to a Spanish monastery, he exchanged the costly ____________________ of a king for the simple habit of a monk.

10. Many a now-forgotten "movie great" has discovered to his or her chagrin that fame may indeed be as ____________________ as a passing shower.

End Set B

Synonyms

*Choose the word or form of the word from this Unit that is the same or most nearly the same in meaning as the **boldface** word or expression in the phrase. Write that word on the line. Use a dictionary if necessary.*

1. given an **agreeable** name ____________
2. a member of a **clique** ____________
3. **ornamented** with high-sounding phrases ____________
4. willingly **abandoned** their prejudices ____________
5. wore silken **apparel** ____________
6. had the **gall** to demand an apology ____________
7. the actress's male **complement** ____________
8. condemned the militia's **depraved** behavior ____________
9. the **dogged** researcher ____________
10. a well-known **despiser of mankind** ____________
11. ignore those **inconsequential** objections ____________
12. the **fleeting** nature of power ____________
13. a **clandestine** midnight meeting ____________
14. lived in a home for the **destitute** ____________
15. prone to **fanciful** get-rich-quick schemes ____________

Antonyms

*Choose the word or form of the word from this Unit that is most nearly opposite in meaning to the **boldface** word or expression in the phrase. Write that word on the line. Use a dictionary if necessary.*

1. a very **grim** lunch meeting ____________
2. **consented** to her suggestion ____________
3. **moderate** increases in profits ____________
4. wears **understated** jewelry ____________
5. **intensify** his anxiety ____________

Writing: Words in Action

Do you think celebrities should become politically active, or should they stay out of politics? In a brief essay, support your opinion with examples from current events, your reading (refer to pages 100–101), or your personal experience. Use at least two details from the passage and three or more words from this Unit.

Vocabulary in Context

*Some of the words you have studied in this Unit appear in **boldface** type. Read the passage below, and then circle the letter of the correct answer for each word as it is used in context.*

The city of Liverpool, England, had no recorded history before 1207, when the **misanthrope** King John commandeered a tiny fishing village as a supply post for his **bestial** wars in Ireland. In 1229, Henry III granted Liverpool municipal self-government and the right to issue by-laws. The city began its long history as a port town when it built its first dock in 1715. A city coat of arms was commissioned to show an eagle or lever bird (a **furtive** mythical bird) carrying a bit of foliage. The word *lever* caused inordinate confusion, and the designer instead created a coat of arms with a cormorant, a sea bird, carrying a bit of seaweed, but the mistake turned out to be **felicitous** as it reflected Liverpool's connection with the sea. By the late 1800s, Liverpool had seven miles of docks.

Liverpool saw many of the great ocean liners during "the golden age of ocean liners." The White Star Line, with the *Titanic* as part of its fleet, had headquarters in Liverpool, and *Liverpool* appeared under the name *Titanic* on the great ship's stern. Many Liverpudlians were part of the ship's crew, including the lookout who called out "iceberg right ahead" and one of the musicians who played as the ship sank.

In 1907, the White Star Line decided to **jettison** its Liverpool operations and move to Southampton, and that was the beginning of the end of Liverpool's domination as a port town. After World War II, the region's manufacturing declined in importance as did its trade with the United States. The region soon became depressed as unemployment and the number of **indigent** people increased. It was not until the Beatles, Liverpool natives, burst onto the music scene in the early 1960s that the city regained its fame.

---

1. A man is a **misanthrope**, if he dislikes
- **a.** boredom
- **b.** water
- **c.** violence
- **d.** people

2. The word **bestial** most nearly means
- **a.** unfair
- **b.** unpopular
- **c.** brutal
- **d.** proud

3. A bird that is **furtive**, as the lever is said to be, is
- **a.** secretive
- **b.** hidden
- **c.** under cover
- **d.** on the run

4. The mistake with the coat of arms is **felicitous** because it is
- **a.** fortunate
- **b.** unlucky
- **c.** appropriate
- **d.** unnecessary

5. To **jettison** is to
- **a.** cast off
- **b.** raise up
- **c.** divide
- **d.** expand

6. The word **indigent** most nearly means
- **a.** unhealthy
- **b.** unlucky
- **c.** destitute
- **d.** employed

UNIT 8

*Read the following passage, taking note of the **boldface** words and their contexts. These words are among those you will be studying in Unit 8. It may help you to complete the exercises in this Unit if you refer to the way the words are used below.*

A Passage to Power

<Interview>

Whoever is Speaker of the U.S. House of Representatives sets House rules, adjudicates procedural conflicts, and strives to maintain civility during debates. The Speaker also exerts behind-the-scenes powers by appointing committee chairs and setting the timetables for legislative votes. To learn more about the post and its evolution, we asked the noted congressional scholar, Bill T. Kanoho, about one of the most powerful government posts.

Q: What are the requirements for the Speaker's job?

A: You must be at least 25 years old, a U.S. citizen for the previous seven years, and an inhabitant of the state you are to represent at the time of election.

Q: That's it?

A: That's what the Constitution requires. Another aspect of the post—it's slightly **macabre**—is that the Speaker is second in line, after the Vice President, to the presidency if the President can no longer serve.

Paul Ryan, Speaker of the House, 2016

Q: How do other representatives view the Speaker?

A: It's **irrefutable** that the House reveres its Speaker. After all, it's a very important position. Money talks: From the First Congress onwards, the Speaker always made more money than members of Congress. For example, in 2011, the Speaker was paid $223,500 and members of Congress $174,000.

Q: Was the role of the Speaker always as influential as it is today?

A: Actually, no. The first speaker, Frederick Muhlenberg of Pennsylvania, did little that would **portend** the post would ever grow in importance. It has become **saturated** with power, but I would say a **paucity** of change marked the role until the Twelfth Congress (1811–1813).

Q: Why so little change in those early years?

A: It wasn't that the Speakers were **lackadaisical**, and in fact I believe they all saw the expanding nation as a **juggernaut** on the world stage. But it seems the first Speakers wanted to **conciliate** the members, perhaps because in the early days of our republic fistfights could erupt when one member refused to **recant** a position that angered another.

Q: Why did the job start to change?

A: Henry Clay of Kentucky stirred the pot when he served six nonconsecutive terms as Speaker, from 1811 through 1825, and made a **litany** of changes. The biggest were that he participated in debates, and he enforced strict rules of order to **slough** off attempts to **countermand** his efforts to raise the office to a new **echelon**.

Q: Is that when the job's scope became as powerful as it is today?

A: Well, after Clay left, the office returned to its original scope until 1880, when the Speaker's role was expanded to include being Chairman of the Committee on Rules, a power-filled position.

Q: Then what happened?

A: Maine's Thomas Brackett Reed is what happened. While serving as Speaker from 1889 to 1891, then again from 1895 to 1899, he made **arrant** and successful bids to increase the Speaker's power. The most notable change occurred when he masterminded how to prevent the minority party from using parliamentary maneuvers—that is, exploiting legal technicalities—to block majority party decisions.

Q: Is that when the post became truly powerful?

A: It's been evolving since then. However, it would be **fatuous** not to mention the post's current partisan profile: Republicans and Democrats sometimes have a hard time working together, so a powerful Speaker is needed in order to get things done. And sometimes problems in Congress are **exacerbated** by talking heads—talk show guests and politicians who talk in sound bites that tell only half the story and thus misrepresent an issue.

Q: What can the Speaker do to solve that problem?

A: He or she can be fair. Though politicians may pontificate and argue and attack others' positions, many voters fail to realize this is part of the game. These officials strike a pose to appeal to their constituents, then they get down to business. A lot of friendly **badinage** goes on in the House. Our elected officials are not about to **raze** the Capitol building. The Speaker wouldn't allow it!

Frederick Muhlenberg, circa 1790, was the first Speaker of the House and represented Pennsylvania.

Audio

For iWords and audio passages, go to **SadlierConnect.com**.

Speaker Henry Clay served six nonconsecutive two-year terms as Speaker and made changes that started the post's evolution to what it is today.

Definitions

Note the spelling, pronunciation, part(s) of speech, and definition(s) of each of the following words. Then write the appropriate form of the word in the blank space in the illustrative sentence(s) following.

1. arrant (ar′ ənt)
(*adj.*) thoroughgoing, out-and-out; shameless, blatant

In Shakespeare's tragedy the audience sees clearly that Iago is an ________________ scoundrel, but Othello is blind to his treachery.

2. conciliate (kən sil′ ē āt)
(*v.*) to overcome the distrust of, win over; to appease, pacify; to reconcile, make consistent

Because of the weakness of our army, we had to try to ________________ the enemy.

3. echelon (esh′ ə län)
(*n.*) one of a series of grades in an organization or field of activity; an organized military unit; a steplike formation or arrangement

Although the civil servant began in the lower ________________ of government service, he rose quickly through the ranks.

4. exacerbate (eg zas′ ər bāt)
(*v.*) to make more violent, severe, bitter, or painful

Shouting and name-calling are sure to ________________ any quarrel.

5. irrefutable (ir i fyü′ tə bəl)
(*adj.*) impossible to disprove; beyond argument

The jury felt the prosecution presented it with ________________ evidence of the defendant's guilt.

6. litany (lit′ ə nē)
(*n.*) a prayer consisting of short appeals to God recited by the leader alternating with responses from the congregation; any repetitive chant; a long list

Whenever she talks about her childhood, she recites an interminable ________________ of grievances.

7. paucity (pô′ sə tē)
(*n.*) an inadequate quantity, scarcity, dearth

The senate campaign was marred by a ________________ of original ideas.

8. raze (rāz)
(*v.*) to tear down, destroy completely; to cut or scrape off or out

The town ________________ the old schoolhouse to make room for a larger, more modern school complex.

9. saturate (sach′ ə rāt)
(*v.*) to soak thoroughly, fill to capacity; to satisfy fully
A sponge that is ____________ with water swells up but does not drip.

10. saturnine (sat′ ər nīn)
(*adj.*) of a gloomy or surly disposition; cold or sluggish in mood
Ebenezer Scrooge, of Dickens's *A Christmas Carol*, has a decidedly ____________ temperament.

Using Context

*For each item, determine whether the **boldface** word from pages 114–115 makes sense in the context of the sentence. Circle the item numbers next to the six sentences in which the words are used correctly.*

1. The new coach's **arrant** disregard for the rules and traditions of the league was shocking to the referees.
2. To make French toast, **saturate** bread in a mixture of beaten egg and milk, and then fry the bread in butter or oil.
3. The bright red scarf was the perfect choice to complete the television host's **saturnine** outfit.
4. When the children found out that someone else had adopted the kitten they wanted, nothing could **conciliate** them—not even seeing the other available cats.
5. Nobel Prize winners include scientists who have made extraordinary achievements and rank in the highest **echelon** of their field.
6. Although our argument for increasing the recreation committee's budget seemed **irrefutable** to us, the township denied our request.
7. The judge will now withdraw to her chambers to determine a suitable **litany** for the crime.
8. The injuries that the driver and passengers suffered in the car accident will take a long time to **exacerbate**.
9. Thanks to the **paucity** of snow this year, our area's ski resorts are reporting excellent conditions.
10. It was sad to see the construction crew **raze** the old hotel, but the new high-rise office building will bring much-needed activity to the downtown area.

Choosing the Right Word

*Select the **boldface** word that better completes each sentence. You might refer to the passage on pages 112–113 to see how most of these words are used in context. Note that the choices might be related forms of the Unit words.*

1. Because cherry blossoms are symbols of friendship, Japanese art is (**saturated, conciliated**) with images of boughs laden with the pale pink and white flowers.

2. The defense attorney succeeded in portraying the genial witness as a(n) (**arrant, saturnine**) liar, whose testimony was never credible.

3. The dog's owner (**exacerbated, razed**) the situation when she flagrantly encouraged the terrier to romp in the neighbor's petunias.

4. The views of the two parties involved in this dispute are so diametrically opposed that it will be almost impossible to (**conciliate, saturate**) them.

5. His debating technique is rooted in the firm belief that anything bellowed in a loud voice is absolutely (**arrant, irrefutable**).

6. Over the years, hard work and unstinting devotion to duty have raised me from one (**echelon, litany**) of company management to the next.

7. Someone with such a(n) (**irrefutable, saturnine**) outlook on life doesn't make an agreeable traveling companion, especially on a long journey.

8. It is a good deal easier to (**raze, exacerbate**) an old building than it is to destroy a time-honored social institution.

9. We have many capable and well-meaning people in our organization, but it seems to me that there is a(n) (**paucity, echelon**) of real leadership.

10. By denying your guilt without offering any explanation of your actions, you will only (**saturate, exacerbate**) an already bad situation.

11. I never ask anyone, "How are you?" anymore because I am afraid I will be treated to an endless (**litany, paucity**) of symptoms and ailments.

12. Only a(n) (**arrant, saturnine**) knave would be capable of devising such an incredibly underhanded and treacherous scheme.

Completing the Sentence

Choose the word from the word bank that best completes each of the following sentences. Write the correct word or form of the word in the space provided.

arrant	**echelon**	**irrefutable**	**paucity**	**saturate**
conciliate	**exacerbate**	**litany**	**raze**	**saturnine**

1. At first I thought it would be easy to shoot holes in their case, but I soon realized that their arguments were practically ____________________.

2. "I find it terribly depressing to be around people whose dispositions are so ____________________ and misanthropic," I remarked.

3. Though some "home remedies" appear to alleviate the symptoms of a disease, they may in fact ____________________ the condition.

4. My shirt became so ____________________ with perspiration on that beastly day that I had to change it more than once during the match.

5. The breaking news story concerned corruption among the highest ____________________ of politics.

6. Her friendly manner and disarming smile helped to ____________________ those who opposed her views on the proposal.

7. "It seems to me that such ____________________ hypocrisy is indicative of a thoroughly opportunistic approach to running for office," I said sadly.

8. His four disastrous years in office were marked by a plenitude of promises and a(n) ____________________ of performance.

9. The service in honor of the miners trapped in the underground collapse included prayers and ____________________.

10. We object to the policy of ____________________ historic old buildings to make way for unsightly parking lots.

End Set A

Definitions

Note the spelling, pronunciation, part(s) of speech, and definition(s) of each of the following words. Then write the appropriate form of the word in the blank space in the illustrative sentence(s) following.

1. allege (ə lej′)
(*v.*) to assert without proof or confirmation
The newspaper tabloid ____________ that the movie star and the director were having creative differences.

2. badinage (bad ə näzh′)
(*n.*) light and playful conversation
I enjoy the delightful ____________ between stars like Spencer Tracy and Katharine Hepburn in 1940s movies.

3. countermand (kau̇n′ tər mand)
(*v.*) to cancel or reverse one order or command with another that is contrary to the first
Today's directive clearly ____________ all previous instructions on how to exit the building in case of fire.

4. fatuous (fach′ ü əs)
(*adj.*) stupid or foolish in a self-satisfied way
In order to discredit the candidate, the columnist quoted some of his more ____________, self-serving remarks.

5. juggernaut (jəg′ ər nôt)
(*n.*) a massive and inescapable force or object that crushes whatever is in its path
Any population that has experienced the ____________ of war firsthand will not easily forget its destructive power.

6. lackadaisical (lak ə dā′ zə kəl)
(*adj.*) lacking spirit or interest, halfhearted
The team's performance in the late innings was ____________ because they were so far ahead.

7. macabre (mə käb′)
(*adj.*) grisly, gruesome; horrible, distressing; having death as a subject
The continuing popularity of horror movies suggests that one way to score at the box office is to exploit ____________ situations.

8. portend (por tənd′)
(*v.*) to indicate beforehand that something is about to happen; to give advance warning of
In Shakespeare's plays, disturbances in the heavens usually ____________ disaster or trouble in human affairs.

9. recant (ri kant′)

(*v.*) to withdraw a statement or belief to which one has previously been committed, renounce, retract

On the stand, the defendant ____________________ the guilty admissions she had made in her confession to the police.

10. slough (sləf)

(*v.*) to cast off, discard; to get rid of something objectionable or unnecessary; to plod through as if through mud; (*n.*) a mire; a state of depression

At New Year's time, many people resolve to ____________________ off bad habits and live better.

The advancing line of tanks became bogged down in a ____________________.

Using Context

*For each item, determine whether the **boldface** word from pages 118–119 makes sense in the context of the sentence. Circle the item numbers next to the six sentences in which the words are used correctly.*

1. Her **lackadaisical** attitude about the interview showed that she did not want the job.
2. I would work overtime, but I could not possibly **slough** on another responsibility.
3. He attempted to **recant** the inventory which listed all of the items that were sold.
4. Edgar Allan Poe wrote prose with **macabre** themes, such as death, terror, and insanity.
5. Her demeanor is so **fatuous** that she seems to be the likely choice to be the next queen.
6. The musical score became gloomier and more ominous to **portend** the arrival of the villain.
7. I don't know how I would get through the workday without the **badinage** between my coworkers and myself.
8. The defense claimed that the police were too quick to **allege** that they had the right suspect—that the evidence was scant.
9. The fickle pop star was known to make specific demands for her dressing room, only to **countermand** those directions and make more ridiculous requests.
10. In the business world, he is known as a **juggernaut**, one who can negotiate well with others and treat them fairly.

Set B

Choosing the Right Word

*Select the **boldface** word that better completes each sentence. You might refer to the passage on pages 112–113 to see how most of these words are used in context. Note that the choices might be related forms of the Unit words.*

1. On the Western Front in August 1914, the French army steeled itself against the oncoming (**badinage, juggernaut**) that was the German Second Army.

2. She excused herself from lending me the money I so desperately needed by (**recanting, alleging**) that she had financial troubles of her own.

3. Economists believe that the drop in automobile sales and steel production (**countermands, portends**) serious problems for business in the future.

4. Our excitement at visiting the world-famous ruins was dampened by the (**lackadaisical, macabre**) attitude of the bored and listless guide.

5. A plunge in atmospheric pressure (**alleges, portends**) an oncoming storm.

6. Ever a bit of a melancholic, Mr. Smithers sank into a (**badinage, slough**) in the wintertime.

7. In earlier times, people whose views conflicted with "received opinion" often had to (**recant, portend**) their ideas or face the consequences.

8. Not surprisingly, the committee's final report was an incongruous mixture of the astute and the (**lackadaisical, fatuous**).

9. The authority of the student council is not absolute because the principal can (**countermand, slough**) any of its decisions.

10. Stephen King's book *Danse* (***Macabre, Fatuous***) surveys popular and obscure horror fiction of the twentieth century.

11. His attempts at casual (**badinage, juggernaut**) did not conceal the fact that he was acutely embarrassed by his blunder.

12. By (**portending, sloughing**) off the artificiality of her first book, the novelist arrived at a style that was simple, genuine, and highly effective.

Completing the Sentence

Choose the word from the word bank that best completes each of the following sentences. Write the correct word or form of the word in the space provided.

allege	**countermand**	**juggernaut**	**macabre**	**recant**
badinage	**fatuous**	**lackadaisical**	**portend**	**slough**

1. The seriousness of the matter under discussion left no room for the type of lighthearted ____________________ encountered in the locker room.

2. The enemy's lines crumpled before the mighty ____________________ of our attack like so much wheat before a harvester.

3. After she made that absurd remark, a(n) ____________________ grin of self-congratulation spread like syrup across her face.

4. You are not going to do well in your job if you continue to work in such a(n) ____________________ and desultory manner.

5. Only someone with a truly ____________________ sense of humor would decide to use a hearse as the family car or a coffin as a bed.

6. Ms. Ryan's warnings to the class to "review thoroughly" seemed to me to ____________________ an unusually difficult examination.

7. No sooner had the feckless tsar decreed a general mobilization than he ____________________ his order, only to reissue it a short time later.

8. The men now being held in police custody are ____________________ to have robbed eight supermarkets over the last year.

9. However much it may cost me, I will never ____________________ the principles to which I have devoted my life.

10. As a snake ____________________ off its old skin, so he hoped to rid himself of his weaknesses and develop a new and better personality.

End Set B

Synonyms

*Choose the word or form of the word from this Unit that is the same or most nearly the same in meaning as the **boldface** word or expression in the phrase. Write that word on the line. Use a dictionary if necessary.*

1. **slog** through the marsh ______________
2. the upper **levels** of power ______________
3. a **listless** response from voters ______________
4. **barrage** of hype ______________
5. tried to **placate** both sides in the dispute ______________
6. **foreshadows** dangers to come ______________
7. **demolished** the neglected properties ______________
8. seemed in a **sullen** mood ______________
9. **unmitigated** nonsense ______________
10. **claimed** that a crime had been committed ______________
11. **revoke** the curfew ______________
12. an idea that **permeates** all aspects of society ______________
13. will **aggravate** tensions between the rivals ______________
14. a long **rigmarole** of questions and answers ______________
15. witty **banter** between the friends ______________

Antonyms

*Choose the word or form of the word from this Unit that is most nearly opposite in meaning to the **boldface** word or expression in the phrase. Write that word on the line. Use a dictionary if necessary.*

1. wore a **cheerful** mask ______________
2. known for his **sensible** opinions ______________
3. an **untenable** position ______________
4. a growing **abundance** of cheap labor ______________
5. has **reaffirmed** her support of free trade ______________

Writing: Words in Action

One challenge for the Speaker is deciding if and when to compromise with other members. Do you think that compromise is often a sign of weakness? Would you ever compromise your principles? Write an expository essay, using at least two details from the passage (pages 112–113) and three or more words from this Unit.

Vocabulary in Context

*Some of the words you have studied in this Unit appear in **boldface** type. Read the passage below, and then circle the letter of the correct answer for each word as it is used in context.*

Visitors to the United States Capitol building in Washington, D.C. are likely to be impressed when they are led into the Senate and House chambers by the tour guide. These elaborately decorated forums, **saturated** in history, are where our lawmakers convene to debate and enact the laws that govern numerous aspects of our lives. The chambers possess an **irrefutable** aura of grandeur.

Washington insiders and students of government, however, know otherwise. The epicenter of the legislative process is not the chamber but the committee system: the approximately 250 smaller units in which Congress frames and discusses a **litany** of new bills and old. And within the most exalted **echelon** of that system is the quaintly named House Committee on Ways and Means.

Records on the Ways and Means Committee **allege** that it is the oldest in Congress, dating back to July 1789. Its power derives from its status as the principal tax-writing committee in the House of Representatives, where, according to Article I, Section 7 of the Constitution, all bills for raising revenue must originate. The committee's scope now extends to banking, tariffs, reciprocal trade agreements, and aspects of Social Security and Medicare, and it is thus safe to conclude that no politico, however **saturnine**, would give an invitation to join Ways and Means a cold shoulder.

It seems likely that the concept of "ways and means" as a method of handling financial issues in a legislature had antecedents in both British and colonial government: scholars have verified that it was used in Parliament and in early colonial legislatures. Today, Ways and Means is a sizable committee, consisting of nearly 10 percent of House members. As with all Congressional committees, the chairperson is from the majority party in the House.

---

1. If something is **saturated**, it is
a. cleansed **c.** repurposed
b. imbued **d.** tainted

2. The word **irrefutable** most nearly means
a. undeniable **c.** untenable
b. ambiguous **d.** malleable

3. A **litany** is
a. a concession **c.** a designated task
b. a book **d.** a long list

4. The top **echelon** in an organization is the highest
a. rank **c.** prize
b. honor **d.** executive

5. The word **allege** most nearly means
a. proclaim **c.** assert
b. hazard **d.** prove

6. If you are **saturnine** you are
a. gloomy **c.** senile
b. vivacious **d.** gregarious

Read the following passage, taking note of the ***boldface*** *words and their contexts. These words are among those you will be studying in Unit 9. It may help you to complete the exercises in this Unit if you refer to the way the words are used below.*

Security Status: It's Complicated

<Persuasive Essay>

To great **acclamation**, social networking sites, websites that allow connected groups of individuals to interact online, burst onto the scene in the late 1990s. Since then, tell-all social networking sites have increased in popularity exponentially. With some sites boasting hundreds of millions of users disclosing information with total strangers and friends alike, there now exists an extensive online community sharing ideas, interests, and activities.

Social networking is, in theory, an excellent, appealing concept, but risks abound with every online **peregrination**. Sites provide ready access to personal information, so even the most **imperturbable** and experienced users must recognize and be mindful of the hazards.

Social networking sites allow users to keep in touch and build connections without much effort, but who else is effortlessly monitoring their correspondences? Corporations are, for one. Looking for market advantages, businesses use personal information to evaluate potential customers. The companies that own the social networks are, in a sense, in **collusion** with those corporations when they collect data to sell to their advertisers. But the infringements of advertisers are **paltry** problems, more **redolent** of annoying telephone marketing, than of the serious crimes committed by those who prey on social network users. For, unfortunately, along with the rapid growth of sites and their many beneficial applications, there has also emerged a veritable **paroxysm** of criminal activity associated with those sites.

Yes, there are unsavory individuals out there who are very interested in collecting the information that people post. There are identity thieves and those who **vituperatively** harass or stalk people online, or who infect computers with malware; scam artists looking to take advantage of **tyros** and veterans alike. It is another sad truth that there is a growing number of bullying teens who use social networks to cruelly **calumniate** and isolate classmates. In a few cases, cyber-bullying has led to tragedy as victims try to escape their tormentors.

Fortunately, available tools and strategies minimize risks when using social networks. Users must remain as **unremitting** in their efforts to protect their privacy as the malefactors are in theirs to breach it.

The old **shibboleth**, "Leave no stone unturned," is a **mandate** in this war against cyber criminals and against as yet unforeseen issues. Above all, users must be **chary** in what they post, providing only necessary information that errs on the side of caution and good sense. Social networkers should limit personal data in postings and provide more details in secure areas. Nobody really wants strangers to have his or her phone number or address. Remember, personal data are valuable to crooks, identity thieves, spammers, and advertisers.

Furthermore, users should familiarize themselves with a site's privacy settings and be alert to changes in them. It is a good practice to reject requests to connect with strangers looking for money. If a social network account is compromised, it should be reported to the site and the account should be closed. Protective strategies are not **pedantry**, but key components of a prudent approach to safe social networking. Social networkers must proceed with caution and common sense to enjoy the many benefits of cyber-communities.

Audio

For iWords and audio passages, go to **SadlierConnect.com**.

Definitions

Note the spelling, pronunciation, part(s) of speech, and definition(s) of each of the following words. Then write the appropriate form of the word in the blank space in the illustrative sentence(s) following.

1. acclamation (ak lə mā′ shən)
(*n.*) a shout of welcome; an overwhelming verbal vote of approval
It is very rare for a presidential candidate to be nominated by ____________ from the convention floor.

2. chary (châr′ ē)
(*adj.*) extremely cautious, hesitant, or slow (to); reserved, diffident
Since so many funds had been spent with so few results, they were ____________ about appropriating more money.

3. dilettante (dil′ ə tänt)
(*n.*) a dabbler in the arts; one who engages in an activity in an amateurish, trifling way; (*adj.*) superficial
Many people dismissed the poster artists of the 1960s as mere ____________ with nothing serious to say about life or art.

4. imperturbable (im pər tər′ bə bəl)
(*adj.*) not easily excited; emotionally steady
The witness remained ____________ throughout the grueling cross-examination.

5. paroxysm (par′ ək siz əm)
(*n.*) a sudden outburst; a spasm, convulsion
The children greeted the clown with a ____________ of laughter when he began making his funny faces.

6. pedantry (ped′ ən trē)
(*n.*) a pretentious display of knowledge; overly rigid attention to rules and details
The fussy music professor was distinguished more for her ____________ than her true scholarship.

7. redolent (red′ ə lənt)
(*adj.*) fragrant, smelling strongly; tending to arouse memories or create an aura
My grandmother's kitchen was alway ____________ with the smells of baking.

8. refulgent (ri fəl′ jənt)
(*adj.*) shining, radiant, resplendent
The swift-flowing stream beside our house was ____________ in the morning light.

9. tyro (tī' rō) — (*n.*) a beginner, novice; one with little or no background or skill

You cannot expect a mere ____________________ to perform like a veteran in his first season of major league play.

10. unremitting (ən ri mit' iŋ) — (*adj.*) not stopping, maintained steadily, never letting up, relentless

The social laws in Edith Wharton's novels are ____________________.

Using Context

For each item, determine whether the **boldface** *word from pages 126–127 makes sense in the context of the sentence. Circle the item numbers next to the six sentences in which the words are used correctly.*

1. The mournful hooting of an owl and lengthening late afternoon shadows added to the **chary** atmosphere of the old graveyard.

2. The **refulgent** bursts of green, white, red, and blue in quick succession at the end of the fireworks show thrilled the crowd.

3. He is now studying international affairs at a graduate level and hopes someday to work as a **dilettante**.

4. It's hard to believe that someone who is a **tyro** at knitting could have made that beautiful scarf.

5. You should avoid phrases such as *added bonus* and *basic fundamentals* because they are **redolent**.

6. This gentle, **imperturbable** horse is perfect for beginning riders.

7. The charitable organization is hosting a banquet next month to thank its donors for their generous **pedantry**.

8. Suffering from an upper respiratory infection, the speaker could not get far into her presentation without breaking out into a **paroxysm** of coughing.

9. The winner of the most valuable player award had to wait for the audience's **acclamation** to subside before beginning his acceptance speech.

10. Because of the **unremitting** noise of construction on my street, I decided to go to the library to study for my biology exam.

Choosing the Right Word

*Select the **boldface** word that better completes each sentence. You might refer to the passage on pages 124–125 to see how most of these words are used in context. Note that the choices might be related forms of the Unit words.*

1. Many of the most well-known paintings of Grandma Moses portray rural scenes that are (**redolent, unremitting**) of her childhood in upstate New York.

2. Isn't it sheer (**pedantry, refulgence**) on his part to use terms like *Proustian* and *Kafkaesque* when he knows they mean nothing to his audience?

3. It is easy to criticize him, but how can we overlook the fact that for 20 years he has worked (**unremittingly, charily**) to help the homeless?

4. Although Martin thinks he is an expert software developer, many of his dissatisfied clients view him as merely a (**paroxysm, tyro**).

5. I'm not sure if Tom's (**imperturbable, redolent**) spirit is due to toughness or to an inability to understand the dangers of the situation.

6. Once the senator's nomination became a certainty, all opposition to him evaporated, and he was named by (**pedantry, acclamation**).

7. Clad in the (**refulgent, dilettante**) armor of moral rectitude, he sallied forth to do battle with the forces of evil.

8. Although he has been in this business for 20 years, he still has the sublime innocence of the most helpless (**tyro, paroxysm**).

9. Because my teacher is usually so (**chary, imperturbable**) of giving compliments, I felt really good when she spoke well of my essay.

10. Since she comes from a rural area, she expresses herself in language that is (**redolent, refulgent**) of the farm and of country life in general.

11. The same difficulties that serve as a challenge to the true professional will be a crushing discouragement to the typical (**acclamation, dilettante**).

12. A (**paroxysm, pedantry**) of indignation flashed through the community, and the streets filled with angry people ready to protest the proposal.

Completing the Sentence

Choose the word from the word bank that best completes each of the following sentences. Write the correct word or form of the word in the space provided.

acclamation	**dilettante**	**paroxysm**	**redolent**	**tyro**
chary	**imperturbable**	**pedantry**	**refulgent**	**unremitting**

1. Seized by a(n) ________________ of rage, he began to beat the bars of his cell with his bare hands.

2. However long and hard the struggle, we must be ________________ in our efforts to wipe out racism in this country.

3. I have learned from long experience to be extremely ________________ about offering advice when it has not been requested.

4. The scene may seem ordinary to you, but I find it ________________ with memories of happy summers spent in these woods.

5. I thought I was unexcitable, but she is as ________________ as the granite lions in front of the public library.

6. It is sheer ________________ to insist upon applying the rules of formal literary composition to everyday speech and writing.

7. As a(n) ________________ summer sun sank slowly in the west, the skies were ablaze with color.

8. She may have great musical talents, but she will get nowhere as long as she has the casual attitude of the ________________.

9. Since Lucy had expected no more than polite applause, she was delighted by the ________________ she received from the audience.

10. Even the merest ________________ in the use of firearms knows that a gun should never be pointed at another person.

End Set A

Definitions

Note the spelling, pronunciation, part(s) of speech, and definition(s) of each of the following words. Then write the appropriate form of the word in the blank space in the illustrative sentence(s) following.

1. bucolic
(byü käl′ ik)

(*adj.*) characteristic of the countryside, rural; relating to shepherds and cowherds, pastoral

Elizabethans who wrote of shepherds in country settings were imitating the Greek ____________________ poets.

2. calumniate
(kə ləm′ nē āt)

(*v.*) to slander; to accuse falsely and maliciously

Not only did the artist's enemy seek to discredit her while she was alive but tried to ____________________ her memory as well.

3. collusion
(kə lü′ zhən)

(*n.*) secret agreement or cooperation

It was discovered that senior members of the company had been in ____________________ with the enemy.

4. increment
(in′ krə mənt)

(*n.*) an enlargement, increase, addition

Employees were added to the work force in ____________________ of five to reduce training costs.

5. mandate
(man′ dāt)

(*n.*) an authoritative command, formal order, authorization; (*v.*) to issue such an order

The peacekeepers were sent into the war-torn country under a UN ____________________ to protect civilians.

The state ____________________ that all vehicles undergo an annual inspection.

6. paltry
(pôl′ trē)

(*adj.*) trifling, insignificant; mean, despicable; inferior, trashy

The billionaire was so greedy that he contributed only a ____________________ sum of money to charity each year.

7. peregrination
(per ə grə nā′ shən)

(*n.*) the act of traveling; an excursion, especially on foot or to a foreign country

After returning from my ____________________ throughout South America, I wrote a book about my experiences.

8. shibboleth
(shib′ ə leth)

(*n.*) a word, expression, or custom that distinguishes a particular group of persons from all others; a commonplace saying or truism

Most voters are tired of hearing the same old promises and ____________________ in election campaigns.

9. vacillate (vas′ ə lāt)

(*v.*) to swing indecisively from one idea or course of action to another; to waver weakly in mind or will

Someone who ________________ in a crisis should not be in a position of leadership.

10. vituperative (vī tü′ pər ə tiv)

(*adj.*) harshly abusive, severely scolding

That ________________ speech in which she blamed others for her own mistakes may have cost her the election.

Using Context

*For each item, determine whether the **boldface** word from pages 130–131 makes sense in the context of the sentence. Circle the item numbers next to the six sentences in which the words are used correctly.*

1. The geometry problem called for identifying the shape in which the angle had increased by an **increment** of 30 degrees.
2. You have shown such **peregrination** in the face of so much opposition that we would like you to teach a course on dealing with difficult people.
3. The new policy will **mandate** that all employees participate in the company's social responsibility program by volunteering for a certain number of hours each year.
4. What motivates Hamlet to **vacillate** between avenging his father's death and taking no action at all?
5. Everyone believed that the criminal must have been working in **collusion** with someone inside the police force and thus was able to stay out of their reach.
6. I say you are "too kind" because of your tendency to **calumniate** me every time I see you.
7. The **vituperative** insults exchanged between the two opponents before the match reflected poorly upon both of them.
8. The **bucolic** sound of blaring police sirens and taxi horns on the city streets outside can be rather disruptive during our meetings.
9. She displayed such **shibboleth** at the mere suggestion of taking the bus instead of a taxi that I immediately assumed her to be a snob.
10. The **paltry** amount of rain over the past few months has caused my garden to become barren and withered.

Choosing the Right Word

*Select the **boldface** word that better completes each sentence. You might refer to the passage on pages 124–125 to see how most of these words are used in context. Note that the choices might be related forms of the Unit words.*

1. During our family's recent (**peregrination, shibboleth**) to the New Orleans French Quarter, we attended several jazz concerts.
2. It has long been known that some twisted and unhappy people derive a kind of satisfaction from (**calumniating, colluding**) others.
3. The phrase "We the people" in the Constitution indicates that the ultimate (**mandate, vacillation**) of our government comes from the popular will.
4. Perhaps he would be less lyrical about the delights of the (**bucolic, paltry**) life if, like me, he had grown up on a farm in Kansas.
5. During the course of my (**peregrinations, collusions**) through the world of books, I have picked up all kinds of useful information.
6. Are we to try to make a realistic analysis of our alternatives or let ourselves be distracted by slogans and (**mandates, shibboleths**)?
7. The gambler's predictions of the game scores were so incredibly accurate that we suspected some form of (**increment, collusion**).
8. If we (**vacillate, calumniate**) now at adopting a tough energy policy, we may find ourselves in a desperate situation in the future.
9. I am perfectly willing to listen to a reasonable complaint, but I will not put up with that kind of (**bucolic, vituperative**) backbiting.
10. The senate candidate claimed that her opponent's most recent television ad (**calumniated, vacillated**) her husband and children.
11. Not satisfied with the slow (**increment, peregrination**) of his savings in a bank account, he turned to speculation in the stock market.
12. How do you have the nerve to offer such a (**paltry, vituperative**) sum for this magnificent "antique" car!

Completing the Sentence

Choose the word from the word bank that best completes each of the following sentences. Write the correct word or form of the word in the space provided.

bucolic	**collusion**	**mandate**	**peregrination**	**vacillate**
calumniate	**increment**	**paltry**	**shibboleth**	**vituperative**

1. "The overwhelming victory I have won at the polls," the Governor-elect said, "has given me a clear ________________ to carry out my program."

2. Since Lincoln is now considered a great national hero, it is hard to believe that he was bitterly ________________ when he was President.

3. Every time I sign a new lease on my apartment, my rent goes up, though the ________________ are not usually very large.

4. The painting shows a restfully ________________ scene, with some cows grazing placidly in a meadow as their shepherd dozes under a bush.

5. As we waited through the long night for the arrival of the rescue party, we ________________ between hope and despair.

6. In my various ________________ through that vast metropolis, I ran across many curious old buildings that the ordinary tourist never sees.

7. I had expected a decent tip from the party of six that I waited on early that evening, but all I got was a(n) ________________ two bucks!

8. In a series of searing orations, filled with the most ________________ language, Cicero launched the full battery of political invective against the hapless Mark Antony.

9. The Pledge of Allegiance is no mere ________________ to be recited mechanically and without understanding like some advertising jingle.

10. The contractor was suspected of having acted in ________________ with a state official to fix the bids on certain public works contracts.

End Set B

Synonyms

*Choose the word or form of the word from this Unit that is the same or most nearly the same in meaning as the **boldface** word or expression in the phrase. Write that word on the line. Use a dictionary if necessary.*

1. kept up the **constant** pressure to surrender ____________
2. a **journey** through the mountains ____________
3. a severe sneezing **fit** ____________
4. a stunningly **luminous** smile ____________
5. labeled a mere **trifler** by the experts ____________
6. bored us with his **hairsplitting** ____________
7. **defamed** by my opponent ____________
8. in **cahoots** with the competition ____________
9. keeps repeating the tired old **catchphrases** ____________
10. large **gain** in tax revenues ____________
11. many mistakes made by the **neophyte** ____________
12. must obey the **directive** ____________
13. painted a charming **country** scene ____________
14. **seesawed** in their commitments ____________
15. **wary** of flattery and favor-seekers ____________

Antonyms

*Choose the word or form of the word from this Unit that is most nearly opposite in meaning to the **boldface** word or expression in the phrase. Write that word on the line. Use a dictionary if necessary.*

1. afraid of the **laudatory** comments ____________
2. **unevocative** of the smells of the countryside ____________
3. **unflappable** despite the criticism ____________
4. the **jeers** of the audience ____________
5. a **colossal** amount of debt ____________

Writing: Words in Action

Educate the public about the potential dangers of social networking sites. Write a letter to the editor that persuades parents to take steps to ensure their young children use such sites appropriately and safely. Use examples from your reading (pages 124–125) and three or more words from this Unit.

Vocabulary in Context

*Some of the words you have studied in this Unit appear in **boldface** type. Read the passage below, and then circle the letter of the correct answer for each word as it is used in context.*

The beauty of the Internet is its accessibility to anyone with a computer, and it is precisely this accessibility that threatens the safety of all computer systems. As the world shifts into a digital age, information is increasingly threatened by anonymous hackers around the globe. Formerly the territory of the federal government and the military, cyberattacks are currently on the rise in the private sector. In a recent poll, 83 percent of multinational corporations believed that they had been the target of an attack—this number was up 20.6 percent from the previous year, which is a drastic **increment** by any metric. Some consultants assert that 92 percent of companies have experienced a cyberattack in their history.

Hackers come in all forms: a savvy teenager in a **bucolic** setting cannot be dismissed as a **dilettante** because that person can cause as much damage as a hacker in **collusion** with a nation-state who exploits classified information illegally obtained from other governments. Malicious hackers are called "black hats"—a name derived from old Western films when the nefarious villains could be discerned by the color of their hats. Yet not all hackers steal identities, damage critical infrastructure, or unearth confidential government correspondence: "white hats" help companies by looking for bugs or vulnerabilities in websites that can be exploited by black hats. Many prominent corporations in pristine, **refulgent** offices hire white-hat hackers to locate the bugs that could make their companies prone to a cyberattack. This course of action is one from which corporate leaders may not **vacillate** as attacks become more sophisticated and effective.

Hacking is a complex, global concern that requires a multifaceted solution as intricate as the problem itself. Since there is no prescription for making the Internet secure, white hats are a start: using the nation's computer geniuses in beneficial ways can help combat the geniuses who cause catastrophic destruction.

---

1. An **increment** of 20.6 percent is
- **a.** an exception
- **b.** a prohibition
- **c.** a modification
- **d.** an increase

2. A **bucolic** setting is
- **a.** rural
- **b.** suburban
- **c.** over-populated
- **d.** urban

3. A **dilettante** generally engages in activities in
- **a.** a detached way
- **b.** a disorganized way
- **c.** an attentive way
- **d.** an amateurish way

4. The word **collusion** most nearly means
- **a.** a formal proposal
- **b.** a hidden motive
- **c.** a secret agreement
- **d.** a dangerous union

5. The word **refulgent** most nearly means
- **a.** traditional
- **b.** shining
- **c.** vacant
- **d.** unusual

6. If you **vacillate** you
- **a.** fluctuate
- **b.** arrange
- **c.** explain
- **d.** fight

Vocabulary for Comprehension

Part 1

*Read this passage, which contains words in **boldface** that appear in Units 7–9. Then choose the best answer to each question based on what is stated or implied in the passage. You may refer to the passage as often as necessary.*

Questions 1–10 are based on the following passage.

This passage is adapted from Charles Chestnutt, *The House Behind the Cedars*. Originally published in 1900.

Boundless Time touches all things with a destroying hand; and if he seems now and then to bestow the bloom of youth, the sap of spring, it is but an **ephemeral** mockery, to be surely and swiftly followed by the wrinkles of old age, the dry leaves and bare branches of winter. And yet there are places where Time seems to linger lovingly long after youth has departed, and to which he seems loath to bring the evil day. Who has not known some even-tempered old man or woman who seemed to have drunk of the fountain of youth? Who has not seen somewhere an old town that, having long since ceased to grow, yet held its own without perceptible decline?

Some such trite reflection—as apposite to the subject as most random reflections are—passed through the mind of a young man who came out of the front door of the Patesville Hotel about nine o'clock one fine morning in spring, a few years after the Civil War, and started down Front Street toward the market-house. Arriving at the **bucolic** town late the previous evening, he had been driven up from the steamboat in a carriage, from which he had been able to distinguish only the shadowy outlines of the houses along the street; so that this morning **peregrination** was his first opportunity to see the town by daylight. He was dressed in **raiment** of linen duck—the day was warm—a panama straw hat, and patent leather shoes. In appearance he was tall, dark, with straight, black, lustrous hair, and very clean-cut, high-bred features. When he paused by the clerk's desk on his way out, the day clerk, who had just come on duty, glanced at the register and read the last entry:—

"'JOHN WARWICK, CLARENCE, SOUTH CAROLINA.'

"One of the South Ca'lina bigbugs, I reckon—probably in cotton, or turpentine." The gentleman from South Carolina, walking down the street, glanced about him with a **furtive** look, in which curiosity and affection were mingled with a touch of bitterness. He saw little that was not familiar, or that he had not seen in his dreams a hundred times during the past ten years. There had been some changes, it is true, some melancholy changes, but scarcely anything by way of addition or improvement to counterbalance them. Here and there blackened and dismantled walls and **razed** land marked the place where handsome buildings once had stood, for Sherman's march to the sea had left its **irrefutable** mark upon the town.

A two minutes' walk brought Warwick—the name he had registered under, and as we shall call him—to the market-house, the central feature of Patesville, from both the commercial and the picturesque points of view. Warwick was unable to perceive much change in the market-house. Perhaps the surface of the red brick, long unpainted, had **sloughed** off a little more here and there. There might have been a slight accretion of the moss and lichen on the shingled roof. But the tall tower, **refulgent** with its four-faced clock, rose as majestically and uncompromisingly as though the land had never been subjugated.

1. As it is used in line 4, "ephemeral" most nearly means
A) all-powerful.
B) short-lived.
C) old-fashioned.
D) well-intentioned.

2. What is the effect of making the notion of "time" a proper noun in the first paragraph?
A) It personifies "time."
B) It shows that "time" is omnipotent and invincible.
C) It demonstrates that "time" is destructive and harmful.
D) It illustrates that "time" brings youth and old age.

3. As it is used in line 31, "peregrination" most nearly means
A) a period of relaxation.
B) a bout of strenuous exercise.
C) an excursion on foot.
D) a grueling journey.

4. In the second paragraph (lines 18–44), the author includes a description of the man's dress and appearance in order to
A) prove that John Warwick is conspicuous in Patesville.
B) demonstrate that John Warwick comes from a modest background.
C) compare John Warwick to those whom he meets in Patesville.
D) show that John Warwick has an attractive physical appearance.

5. As it is used in line 59, "razed" most nearly means
A) groomed meticulously.
B) utilized partially.
C) destroyed completely.
D) ignored entirely.

6. The description of the town in the fourth paragraph (lines 63–78) summarizes
A) Warwick's observations about how the past ten years have changed Patesville.
B) Warwick's dreams about how Patesville would look after his ten-year absence.
C) Warwick's descriptions of the positive and negative changes to the town.
D) Warwick's desires to see the beauty in Patesville in spite of its destruction.

7. The author mentions the market-house in the last paragraph in order to
A) demonstrate that the market-house has not changed drastically.
B) show that the tower starkly contrasts its ruined surroundings.
C) document the small changes to the building's exterior and roof.
D) prove that the market-house should be the focal point of Patesville.

8. Which choice provides the best evidence for the answer to the previous question?
A) Lines 63–68 (A two. . . view)
B) Lines 68–72 (Warwick. . .there)
C) Lines 70–74 (Perhaps. . . shingled roof)
D) Lines 74–78 (But the tall. . . subjugated)

9. It can reasonably be inferred from information in the last paragraph that Warwick most likely feels
A) grateful that the tall tower has survived.
B) disappointed upon seeing the market-house.
C) disgusted by the moss on the roof.
D) relieved to reach his destination.

10. Which choice best summarizes the setting of Patesville?
A) An isolated town with houses, hotels, and a splendid market-house
B) A formerly majestic place that has been adversely altered by war
C) A completely blighted town without any redeeming features
D) A town that has been spared from significant external destruction

Vocabulary for Comprehension

Part 2

*Read this passage, which contains words in **boldface** that appear in Units 7–9. Then choose the best answer to each question based on what is stated or implied in the passage. You may refer to the passage as often as necessary.*

Questions 1–10 are based on the following passage.

This passage is adapted from Kate Chopin, "A Pair of Silk Stockings." Originally published in 1897.

Mrs. Sommers one day found herself the unexpected possessor of fifteen dollars; a **paltry** amount for some, but an unexpected windfall in her **indigent** situation. It seemed to her an **inordinate** figure, and this **increment** stuffed and bulged her threadbare wallet and imparted her with a feeling of prominence such as she had not enjoyed for years.

The question of investment was one that occupied her greatly; for a day or two she walked about apparently in a dreamy state, but really absorbed in **unremitting** speculation and calculation. She decided that a dollar or two should be added to the price usually paid for Janie's shoes, which would insure their lasting an appreciable time longer than they usually did. She would buy a sufficient amount of percale for new shirt waists for the boys and Janie and Mag. She had intended to make the old ones do by skillful patching, and she surmised that Mag should have another gown. And still there would be left enough for new stockings—two pairs apiece—and what darning that would save for a while! Even after that expenditure, she could get caps for the boys and sailor-hats for the girls: the vision of her little brood looking refined and dainty and refreshed for once in their lives excited her and made her restless and wakeful with anticipation.

Due to her **paucity** of money, Mrs. Sommers was one who knew the value of bargains; who could stand for hours making her way gradually toward the desired object that was selling below cost. She had the **effrontery** required to elbow her way if need be; she had learned to clutch a piece of goods and hold it and stick to it with persistence and determination until her turn came to be served, no matter when it came.

Although she was a little faint and tired, her malaise did not **portend** what would happen later that afternoon. She had swallowed a light luncheon—no! when she came to think of it, between getting the children fed and making the place immaculate, and preparing herself for the shopping engagement, she had actually forgotten to eat any luncheon at all!

She sat herself upon a revolving stool before a counter that was comparatively deserted, trying to gather strength and courage to charge through an eager multitude. An all-gone limp feeling consumed her and she rested her gloveless hand aimlessly upon the counter. By degrees she grew aware that her hand had encountered something very soothing, very pleasant to touch; when her eyes cast downwards, her hand lay upon a pile of silk stockings. A placard nearby announced that they had been reduced in price from two dollars and fifty cents to one dollar and ninety-eight cents; and a young girl who stood behind the counter ended her **badinage** with another customer to ask if Mrs. Sommers wished to examine their line of silk hosiery. She smiled, just as if she had been asked to scrutinize a tiara of diamonds with the ultimate ambition of purchasing it. But she continued feeling the soft, sheeny luxurious texture of the stockings—with both hands now, holding them up to see them glisten, and to feel them glide serpent-like through her fingers.

1. What is the author's purpose in the first paragraph?
A) To provide information about Mrs. Sommers's character
B) To give details about Mrs. Sommers's family
C) To explain Mrs. Sommers's financial situation
D) To chronicle Mrs. Sommers's fall from prominence

2. As it is used in line 4, "indigent" most nearly means
A) uncomfortable.
B) impoverished.
C) unsustainable.
D) challenging.

3. In the second paragraph (lines 10–32), Mrs. Sommer's thoughts on how she might spend the money summarize her
A) selfish desires for spending the money on frivolous things.
B) unrealistic expectations for a small amount of money.
C) plans for maximizing the money to make her children look tidy.
D) wishes to make her family appear wealthier than they are.

4. As it is used in line 13, "unremitting" most nearly means
A) relentless.
B) selfless.
C) harmless.
D) fearless.

5. As it is used in line 33, "paucity" most nearly means
A) abundance.
B) scarcity.
C) presence.
D) amount.

6. According to the passage, Mrs. Sommers's character can best be described as
A) refined.
B) indecisive.
C) pessimistic.
D) tenacious.

7. Which choice provides the best evidence for the answer to the previous question?
A) Lines 10–14 ("The question … calculation")
B) Lines 38–43 ("She had … came")
C) Lines 53–57 ("She sat … multitude")
D) Lines 71–74 ("She smiled … it")

8. It can reasonably be inferred that the "silk stockings" in the last paragraph are
A) not worth their expensive price.
B) a desirable but unnecessary luxury.
C) pleasant to touch but worthless.
D) fragile and delicate.

9. What central conflict does the author introduce in the last paragraph of the passage?
A) Mrs. Sommers wants the stockings but has not budgeted for them.
B) Mrs. Sommers wants the sales clerk to believe that she is wealthy.
C) Mrs. Sommers is too tired to shop among the multitude.
D) Mrs. Sommers does not have the money required for the stockings.

10. Which choice best summarizes the passage?
A) A woman has delusions of being wealthy that lead to her irresponsible decisions while out shopping.
B) The main character's persistence and determination ultimately become her downfall when she spends all the money on clothing.
C) The main character finds money that might ruin her family instead of helping them.
D) A poor woman gets a windfall of $15 and has to choose between her desires and her family's needs.

Synonyms

*From the word bank below, choose the word that has the same or nearly the same meaning as the **boldface** word in each sentence and write it on the line. You will not use all of the words.*

badinage	**indigent**	**lackadaisical**	**picayune**
bucolic	**irrefutable**	**litany**	**redolent**
furtive	**jettison**	**paltry**	**refulgent**
illusory	**juggernaut**	**pertinacious**	**saturnine**

1. In many gothic novels, a **morose** servant acts as a dark presence in the household. ________________
2. The second song in the musical was a duet in which the lead characters engage in lighthearted **banter**. ________________
3. In 1979, Mother Teresa, a nun who devoted herself to helping the sick and the **destitute**, received a Nobel Peace Prize for her humanitarian work. ________________
4. I feared that the 800-page-long biography would be filled with **trifling** details, but I was surprised to find that it gave an informative overview of the Victorian era. ________________
5. The heavy meal left us feeling bloated and **indolent**. ________________
6. Foxes are active during both daytime and nighttime hours, but they are **surreptitious** creatures and therefore rarely seen. ________________
7. The spot where we camp every summer is **aromatic** with the combined smells of pine trees and sea air. ________________
8. A brief illness forced my brother to **discard** his plan to go ice fishing with our uncle. ________________
9. The children presented their parents with a **catalogue** of reasons for why they should adopt a dog from the local animal shelter. ________________
10. It's surprising to find a sophisticated five-star restaurant in such a **rustic** setting. ________________
11. The **splendid** golden domes atop the palace could be seen from miles away. ________________
12. If you do not change your spending habits, you will never have more than a **meager** amount of money saved up for emergencies. ________________

Two-Word Completions

Select the pair of words that best completes the meaning of each of the following sentences.

1. Only a thoroughgoing ________________ would enjoy castigating other people's behavior in such unremittingly harsh and ________________ language.

a. dilettante … convivial
b. tyro … arrant
c. misanthrope … vituperative
d. pedant … felicitous

2. Though the official is ________________ to have been in cahoots with the swindlers, so far no substantive evidence has been brought forward to prove ________________.

a. alleged … collusion
b. portended … acclamation
c. calumniated … badinage
d. demurred … peregrination

3. The horribly ________________ furnishings sent the shocked homeowner into a(n) ________________ of anger.

a. macabre … increment
b. chary … effrontery
c. garish … paroxysm
d. refulgent … slough

4. The speed with which the Kaiser issued, then ________________, then reissued orders during the crisis was indicative of his essentially weak and ________________ personality.

a. recanted … imperturbable
b. embellished … pertinacious
c. countermanded … vacillating
d. demurred … fatuous

5. In Chaucer's *Canterbury Tales*, twenty-nine travelers from various ________________ of society set out for Canterbury on a pilgrimage to the shrine of Saint Thomas Beckett. At night the ________________ of travelers shares its stories in order to help time pass.

a. litanies … raiment
b. shibboleths … paucity
c. mandates … collusion
d. echelons … coterie

6. At the June 1961 summit meetings in Vienna, President John Kennedy met with his Soviet ________________, Nikita Khrushchev, in an effort to deal with sources of friction between the two superpowers and ________________ international fears that the so-called Cold War was heating up.

a. raiment … mandate
b. coterie … exacerbate
c. shibboleth … conciliate
d. counterpart … allay

7. The ________________ rains had so ________________ the ground over which we passed that it actually squished and gurgled in protest as we trod on it, and our attack had to be postponed until the sun came out again.

a. ephemeral … embellished
b. unremitting … saturated
c. bestial … jettisoned
d. inordinate … razed

Idioms

In "A Passage to Power" (pages 112–113), in a response to a question about the job of Speaker of the House of Representatives, the interviewee notes that Henry Clay, a previous Speaker, "stirred the pot" in several ways. The phrase "stir the pot" is an idiom that means "cause trouble" or "deliberately bring issues to the surface." The interviewee wants to convey that Clay's actions provoked thought about and changes in the Speaker's duties and power.

An **idiom** is a phrase with a figurative, not literal, meaning. Like other figures of speech, idioms create fresh images in the minds of readers or listeners. Sometimes you will be able to figure out an idiom's meaning from context clues. Other times you may need to consult an online or print dictionary to discover or verify an idiom's meaning.

Choosing the Right Idiom

*Read each sentence. Use context clues to figure out the meaning of each idiom in **boldface**. Then write the letter of the definition for the idiom in the sentence.*

1. "Although you might not like the turnip casserole at first," Karen added, "I hope it will **grow on you** after you've had several bites." ________
2. When the **well-heeled** customer took the luxury convertible for a test drive, the salesman began dreaming of a huge commission. ________
3. "Please **lay it on the line** when you tell me what happened," Grandma told the fidgety children as she stared at her shattered crystal vase. ________
4. Derrick's two talkative aunts arrived at the reunion early so that they could have time to **chew the fat**. ________
5. The news story about the protest included a photo of several local residents who are **up in arms** over the road expansion. ________
6. After our dog left muddy paw prints on the kitchen floor, we worked hard to get it **spick and span** again. ________
7. Noting that her father had worked two jobs to pay for her college education, Maria described him as the **salt of the earth**. ________
8. The aging band's concert tour across Europe this summer is likely to be their **swan song**. ________
9. The parade organizers worried that high wind gusts might **play havoc with** the streamers tied to the flag poles. ________
10. The judge vowed not to **split hairs** when he clarifies his ruling in the tax evasion case. ________

a. final performance
b. become increasingly liked
c. a most worthy person
d. argue about small details
e. neat and clean
f. having plenty of money
g. ruin
h. be totally honest
i. angry
j. have a long chat

Classical Roots

clam, claim—to cry out, shout, call

The root *clam* appears in **acclamation** (page 126). The literal meaning of acclamation is "shouting at," but it now suggests "applause" or "an overwhelmingly favorable oral vote." Some other words based on the same root are listed below.

acclaim	**clamorous**	**disclaimer**	**proclamation**
claimant	**declaim**	**irreclaimable**	**reclamation**

From the list of words above, choose the one that corresponds to each of the brief definitions below. Write the word in the blank space in the illustrative sentence below the definition. Use an online or print dictionary if necessary.

1. an official or formal public announcement
The clerk posted the latest mayoral ____________________ at the entrance to City Hall.

2. a person who asserts a right or title
After many years, the estranged son resurfaced as the last ____________________ to the estate.

3. to applaud; to indicate strong approval; noisy and enthusiastic applause
The winning team enjoyed vigorous public ____________________ in a ticker-tape parade.

4. the act of bringing back or restoring to a normal or useful condition (*"to call back"*)
Innovative irrigation techniques have resulted in the ____________________ of much of the desert.

5. a denial or disavowal of responsibility or connection; a formal refusal of one's rights or claims
The manufacturer issued a swift ____________________ after mediocre reviews of its new product.

6. to speak like an orator; to recite in public, make a public speech; to speak bitterly against
The actor would ____________________ lines from Shakespeare in response to any comment.

7. incapable of being reformed; incapable of being rendered useful
That region of the park is nothing more than ____________________ swampland.

8. marked by loud confusion or outcry; noisily insistent (*"crying out"*)
The protesters outside the White House made ____________________ demands for reform.

*Read the following passage, taking note of the **boldface** words and their contexts. These words are among those you will be studying in Unit 10. It may help you to complete the exercises in this Unit if you refer to the way the words are used below.*

What Happened to the Franklin Expedition?

<Magazine Article>

By Simon Devoucoux

The tragic story of the Franklin Expedition began promisingly enough. In 1845, Sir John Franklin and his crew of about 130 set sail with great fanfare from England to the Arctic Ocean to find the fabled Northwest Passage. Franklin, a seasoned Polar explorer, was charged with **reconnoitering** the island mazes and channels of Arctic Canada in search of a route that linked the North Atlantic to the Pacific, a transit that could save many arduous months at sea for ships traveling to the other side of the world. That was the last time Franklin and his men would ever see home, and the expedition is known as one of the most disastrous in history.

Although the expedition was **fraught** with potential dangers, the British Admiralty believed it had planned for all exigencies and addressed all **foibles** that might weaken the expedition. It commissioned two warships, the HMS *Erebus* and HMS *Terror*, both refitted for navigating treacherous ice floes. Each vessel carried provisions for three years—including 2,500 pounds of tea and 9,000 pounds of chocolate!—and each had thousands of books. The officers and crew were clearly not required to **forgo** luxury onboard.

Although the expedition was well stocked, the Royal Navy had not fully reckoned with subzero temperatures and hazardous Arctic conditions. Officers and crew were outfitted in traditional navy uniforms, skimpy outerwear, and woolen gloves—the navy looked **askance** at changes to convention in clothing. It proved impossible for them to adapt to their new environment as the indigenous people, the Inuit, had over

Sir John Franklin led the lost Franklin Expedition, one of the great unsolved mysteries of the nineteenth century.

In 1895, W. Thomas Smith painted how he imagined the end of the Franklin Expedition looked.

centuries. The Inuit, hunter-gatherers who relied on dog sleds for transportation and animal skins for warmth, had become **inured** to the formidable cold.

Before long, the two ships were irrevocably trapped in pack ice. The expedition lay in **shambles**. Franklin perished in 1847, according to notes later found by search teams, and starvation, scurvy and lead poisoning from tinned food **decimated** the crew. Under the **luminous** northern lights, more and more fell victim to disease, hypothermia, and exposure. With their ranks **attenuated**, some of the crew set out on foot to try to reach an outpost of the Hudson Bay Company, but fate was not **benign**, and the crew members died before reaching the outpost.

Three years after the doomed expedition set out, there was still no word. How could the pride of the Royal Navy disappear without a trace? The country mourned Franklin—explorers and adventurers were national heroes and the attention given them by the public bordered on **obsequious**. Lady Jane Franklin campaigned vigorously for search parties to locate her husband and his ships. A reward was offered, and scores of British and American vessels set sail for the unforgiving North. What they eventually found was unsettling: a few graves, disturbing notes that made little sense, then skeletons and a trail of more than 1,000 artifacts, from sextants to silver utensils to Bibles—even some novels. But a string of facts does not add up to the truth.

Newspapers of the day referred to it as the "awful mystery," and the fate of the Franklin Expedition still intrigues us— Franklin was an experienced explorer, not a **charlatan**, and previous expeditions had been trapped in pack ice and survived, so why did his entire crew perish? **Sporadic** attempts are made today to retrace the expedition, locate the two famous shipwrecks, and uncover what really happened to Franklin and his men. But the full truth may lie submerged somewhere in the frozen depths, where it continues to **rebuff** attempts to uncover it.

Simon Devoucoux lives in Newfoundland. He is a regular contributor to Victorian Exploration Quarterly.

Audio

For iWords and audio passages, go to **SadlierConnect.com.**

Definitions

Note the spelling, pronunciation, part(s) of speech, and definition(s) of each of the following words. Then write the appropriate form of the word in the blank space in the illustrative sentence(s) following.

1. attenuate (ə ten′ yü āt)
(*v.*) to make thin or slender; to weaken or lessen in force, intensity, or value

After making sure the wound was clean, the doctor took steps to ____________ the victim's pain.

2. charlatan (shär′ lə tən)
(*n.*) one who feigns knowledge or ability; a pretender, impostor, or quack

The reporter exposed the real estate agent as a ____________ who routinely deceived her customers.

3. decimate (des′ ə māt)
(*v.*) to kill or destroy a large part of

Again and again, Napoleon was able to ____________ the armies of his enemies and lead his men to further victories.

4. forgo (fôr go′)
(*v.*) to do without, abstain from, give up

One of the best, if not the easiest, ways to lose weight is to ____________ dessert.

5. fraught (frôt)
(*adj.*) full of or loaded with; accompanied by

Even with advanced equipment, expeditions to the top of Mt. Everest are still ____________ with danger.

6. obsequious (əb sē′ kwē əs)
(*adj.*) marked by slavish attentiveness; excessively submissive, often for purely self-interested reasons

Jane Austen ridiculed characters who were ____________ to the aristocracy but condescending to their social inferiors.

7. oscillate (äs′ ə lāt)
(*v.*) to swing back and forth with a steady rhythm; to fluctuate or waver

The terrified narrator in Poe's story "The Pit and the Pendulum" watches the dreaded instrument ____________ as it slowly moves toward him.

8. penitent (pen′ ə tənt)
(*adj.*) regretful for one's sins or mistakes; (*n.*) one who is sorry for wrongdoing

The thief was sincerely ____________.

In the Middle Ages, ____________ often confessed their sins publicly and were publicly punished.

9. rebuff (ri bəf′)
(*v.*) to snub; to repel, drive away; (*n.*) a curt rejection, a check
The old man ____________________ his neighbors by refusing all offers of friendship.
Her ____________________ of my invitation was quite rude.

10. shambles (sham′ bəlz)
(*n.*) a slaughterhouse; a place of mass bloodshed; a state of complete disorder and confusion, mess
The burglars made a complete ____________________ of the apartment in their search for money and jewelry.

Using Context

For each item, determine whether the ***boldface*** *word from pages 146–147 makes sense in the context of the sentence. Circle the item numbers next to the six sentences in which the words are used correctly.*

1. The **penitent** look on my brother's face told me that he was not amused by my little prank.

2. We will need to **rebuff** our efforts if we seriously intend to make it to the finals of the fencing tournament.

3. After years of neglect, the activity center, the swimming pool, and the tennis courts were in a state of complete **shambles**.

4. Harry Houdini, the great magician and escape artist, was critical of anyone who claimed to have actual magical or supernatural powers and would take steps to expose that person as a **charlatan**.

5. The scientist said she is worried that the fungal disease spreading among the area's elm trees will eventually **decimate** them.

6. The attorneys who are working on the case will **forgo** their usual fee and defend the client without charge.

7. During takeoff, the plane will steadily **oscillate** and then achieve liftoff.

8. The plot of the famous spy novel was **fraught** with twists and turns.

9. Competitive swimmers work hard to perfect their strokes and move in ways that best **attenuate** the effects of water resistance.

10. The **obsequious** proofreader found several errors that had been overlooked by both the author and the editor.

Set A

Choosing the Right Word

*Select the **boldface** word that better completes each sentence. You might refer to the passage on pages 144–145 to see how most of these words are used in context. Note that the choices might be related forms of the Unit words.*

1. A grandfather clock works by gravity; when the pendulum (**oscillates, rebuffs**), it moves a system of weights attached to the clock's hands.

2. We must never allow our passion for justice to be (**forgone, attenuated**) to mere halfhearted goodwill.

3. The (**decimated, penitent**) youths agreed to work without pay until they could make restitution for the damage their carelessness had caused.

4. Their relationship has been so (**fraught, obsequious**) with strife and malice that I don't see how they can ever patch things up.

5. Imagine the general disappointment when the so-called "miracle cure" was exposed as a fraud promoted by a (**charlatan, penitent**).

6. Do you want to be a ballet dancer enough to (**oscillate, forgo**) all other activities?

7. How could you have the heart to (**rebuff, attenuate**) those people's piteous appeals for aid?

8. During the Civil War the ranks of both armies were (**decimated, oscillated**) as much by disease as by enemy action.

9. The (**penitent, fraught**) young woman begged her mother for forgiveness.

10. Since he is not guided by firm principles, he (**forgoes, oscillates**) between the rival factions, looking for support from both of them.

11. Somehow or other, a bull got into the china shop and turned it into a complete (**shambles, charlatan**).

12. The play featured the stereotypical (**obsequious, fraught**) butler who treated his employer's family with excessive and artificial politeness.

Completing the Sentence

Choose the word from the word bank that best completes each of the following sentences. Write the correct word or form of the word in the space provided.

attenuate	**decimate**	**fraught**	**oscillate**	**rebuff**
charlatan	**forgo**	**obsequious**	**penitent**	**shambles**

1. Though my childhood recollections have been ____________________ by the passage of time, they have not been totally effaced from my memory.

2. During imperial times, the Roman Senate was little more than a collection of ____________________ yes-men, intent upon preserving their own lives by gratifying the emperor's every whim.

3. As all kinds of wild rumors ran rampant through the besieged city, the mood of the populace ____________________ between hope and despair.

4. In a typical James Bond movie, Agent 007 has a series of adventures that are ____________________ with tongue-in-cheek peril.

5. I was totally taken aback when they ____________________ my kind offers of assistance so rudely and nastily.

6. Any "investment counselor" who promises to double your money overnight must be regarded as a(n) ____________________ or a crook.

7. During the fourteenth century, the Black Death suddenly swept across Europe, ____________________ the population and paralyzing everyday life.

8. Unless the title Special Aide to the Assistant Section Manager involves a salary increase, I would just as soon ____________________ it.

9. No doubt she's very sorry she got caught, but that does not mean that she's at all ____________________ about what she did.

10. The riot converted the quiet streets of that suburban community into a ghastly ____________________.

End Set A

Definitions

Note the spelling, pronunciation, part(s) of speech, and definition(s) of each of the following words. Then write the appropriate form of the word in the blank space in the illustrative sentence(s) following.

1. askance (ə skans′)
(*adv.*) with suspicion, distrust, or disapproval
The English teacher looked ____________________ at the notion that students read compendiums of Dickens's novels.

2. benign (bi nīn′)
(*adj.*) gentle, kind; forgiving, understanding; having a favorable or beneficial effect; not malignant
Lincoln's sensitive stepmother had a ____________________ influence on the lonely boy who had lost his mother.

3. cavil (kav′ əl)
(*v.*) to find fault in a petty way, carp; (*n.*) a trivial objection or criticism
I suggest you do not ____________________ over small things but instead focus on what is important.
Despite a few ____________________ I might make, I still find her to be an excellent poet.

4. foible (foi′ bəl)
(*n.*) a weak point, failing, minor flaw
Backbiting is one human ____________________ not likely to be eradicated.

5. inure (in yür′)
(*v.*) to toughen, harden; to render used to something by long subjection or exposure
The Inuit have become ____________________ to the hardships of the long Arctic winters throughout the years.

6. luminous (lü′ mə nəs)
(*adj.*) emitting or reflecting light, glowing; illuminating
Walking under that ____________________ night sky induced in me weighty thoughts not often pondered.

7. obtuse (äb tüs′)
(*adj.*) blunt, not coming to a point; slow or dull in understanding; measuring between 90° and 180°; not causing a sharp impression
The lieutenant was too ____________________ to see the danger and led his men right into the hands of the enemy.

8. peremptory (pə remp′ tə rē)
(*adj.*) having the nature of a command that leaves no opportunity for debate, denial, or refusal; offensively self-assured, dictatorial; determined, resolute
The board members resented the director's ____________________ tone of voice.

9. reconnoiter (rē kə noit′ ər)
(*v.*) to engage in reconnaissance; to make a preliminary inspection
Infantry officers often ask for volunteers to __________________ the terrain ahead before ordering their soldiers to advance.

10. sporadic (spô rad′ ik)
(*adj.*) occurring at irregular intervals, having no set plan or order
The soldiers heard __________________ gunfire from the other side of the river.

Using Context

*For each item, determine whether the **boldface** word from pages 150–151 makes sense in the context of the sentence. Circle the item numbers next to the six sentences in which the words are used correctly.*

1. The **luminous** city skyline, as viewed from the overlook at night, was truly a breathtaking sight.
2. You have some great ideas, but your **peremptory** way of speaking makes it seem as if you don't actually believe in any of them.
3. If you exercise only on **sporadic** occasions, it is not likely that you will see many improvements in your health or fitness level.
4. I like to bestow a **cavil** on each person I meet throughout the day because complimenting others fills me with great joy.
5. Although she has no formal training in child care, her babysitting services are in high demand because of the **benign** effect she has on children.
6. The tenants decided to **reconnoiter** their lease on the apartment for another year.
7. I was nervous that potential employers would look at me **askance** when I explained that the gap in my job history was due to traveling, but they mostly seem impressed and interested.
8. You describe your hot temper as arising from great passion, but other people see it simply as a **foible**.
9. He is an intelligent person, but his lack of social graces gives some people the impression that he is **obtuse**.
10. I plan to **inure** myself into my book club's good graces by bringing dessert this week.

Set B

Choosing the Right Word

*Select the **boldface** word that better completes each sentence. You might refer to the passage on pages 144–145 to see how most of these words are used in context. Note that the choices might be related forms of the Unit words.*

1. All angles are classified as acute, right, (**obtuse, benign**), or straight, according to the number of degrees they measure.

2. Though I admire the woman's strong points, I find her (**cavils, foibles**) comic.

3. When I found that people I admired were looking (**askance, sporadically**) at my unconventional clothing, I resolved to remedy the situation.

4. Though the small nation was always ready to settle a conflict peacefully, it was not afraid to use (**luminous, peremptory**) force when necessary.

5. Bank robbers often spend a good deal of time (**reconnoitering, inuring**) the neighborhood where the bank they intend to rob is located.

6. Was it Juan's gentle stroking of the frightened dog's neck that produced a (**benign, peremptory**) change in the animal's mood?

7. Since he didn't want to give me credit for having done a good job, he took refuge in endless (**foibles, cavils**) about my work.

8. Over the years, her (**luminous, obtuse**) descriptions and scintillating wit have helped her students master the difficult subject she taught.

9. Although the judge offered two minor (**foibles, cavils**) about our choreography, our dance troupe won first place in the competition.

10. I have learned that (**sporadic, peremptory**) sessions of intense "cramming" can never take the place of a regular study program.

11. Even though my experiences in battle have (**inured, reconnoitered**) me to scenes of suffering, I was horrified by the devastation wrought by the tornado.

12. We believe that classes taught by teachers with specialized training will have a (**sporadic, benign**) effect on the troubled children.

Completing the Sentence

Choose the word from the word bank that best completes each of the following sentences. Write the correct word or form of the word in the space provided.

askance	**cavil**	**inure**	**obtuse**	**reconnoiter**
benign	**foible**	**luminous**	**peremptory**	**sporadic**

1. His statements have been so uniformly ____________________ that I get the impression that he is wearing a permanent pair of mental blinders.

2. I was relieved to learn that the officials were ____________________ and that I would only have to pay a small fine.

3. The general sent scouts on ahead of the army to ____________________ the area for a suitable site to pitch camp.

4. Although the moon appears to be a(n) ____________________ body, the fact is that it only reflects light from the sun.

5. Though critics ____________________ at minor faults in the new Broadway show, the general public loved it.

6. We look ____________________ at any program that makes it harder for city dwellers to get out and enjoy the beauties of nature.

7. Although there had been some ____________________ fighting earlier, the real battles of the Civil War did not begin until Bull Run in July 1861.

8. Good supervisors know that they can get more cooperation from their staff by making polite requests than by issuing ____________________ orders.

9. Life on the family farm has ____________________ me to hard physical labor and long hours of unremitting toil.

10. The woman's personality was a strange mixture of strengths and weaknesses, fortes and ____________________.

End Set B

Synonyms

*Choose the word or form of the word from this Unit that is the same or most nearly the same in meaning as the **boldface** word or expression in the phrase. Write that word on the line. Use a dictionary if necessary.*

1. solution **diluted** with water ______________
2. **quibble** over who is at fault ______________
3. embarrassed by his **stupid** questions ______________
4. a town **devastated** by the flood ______________
5. a **salutary** effect on consumer confidence ______________
6. his **high-handed** challenge to our authority ______________
7. looked **skeptically** at their proposals ______________
8. exposed him as a complete **fraud** ______________
9. feeling **sorry** about the decision ______________
10. become **accustomed** to pain ______________
11. willing to overlook its **defects** ______________
12. **rife** with drama ______________
13. will **spurn** his offer of marriage ______________
14. left the kitchen in **chaos** ______________
15. **vacillated** between two choices ______________

Antonyms

*Choose the word or form of the word from this Unit that is most nearly opposite in meaning to the **boldface** word or expression in the phrase. Write that word on the line. Use a dictionary if necessary.*

1. an **opaque** diamond ______________
2. **overlooked** by the enemy forces ______________
3. the **assertive** assistant's service ______________
4. **indulge in** gossip ______________
5. **continuous** outbreaks of violence ______________

Writing: Words in Action

Suppose that it is 1845 and you are a member of Franklin's crew. You want to write a letter to your family members explaining the goal of the expedition and letting them know how you feel as you depart England. Use at least two details from the passage (pages 144–145) and three or more words from this Unit.

Vocabulary in Context

*Some of the words you have studied in this Unit appear in **boldface** type. Read the passage below, and then circle the letter of the correct answer for each word as it is used in context.*

"The greatest scientific traveler of my time," rhapsodized one of his most distinguished scientific contemporaries. No other person of the era, excepting Napoleon, garnered more fame. Fully three hundred plants were named after him, as well as over one hundred animals, the Humboldt Current in the Pacific Ocean, and a mountain on the moon.

Born into a wealthy, aristocratic Prussian family, Alexander von Humboldt (1769–1859) realized early on that scientific exploration was his calling. He would **oscillate** between a number of destinations before finally settling on South America. Landing at Cunamá (in present-day Venezuela) in July 1799, together with his traveling companion, the French botanist Aimé Bonpland, Humboldt did not **cavil** about his expedition's goals: he would study everything, from soil composition to river systems to volcanic activity to mammalogy. Any lesser goal, he reasoned with **peremptory** logic, would be **obtuse.**

Not only did Humbodt achieve these ambitious goals, but in a **luminous** career full of firsts, he became the preeminent naturalist of his time. Humboldt pioneered the concept of ecosystems, in which all organisms are related in an interdependent web of life. He invented isotherms, the lines used on maps to link regions with the same average temperature and air pressure. Scarcely **penitent** about the boldness of his theories, he postulated an ancient connection between South America and Africa, thus foreshadowing plate tectonic theory. Humboldt was the first to argue that climates were the product of a perpetual interrelationship between land, ocean, wind, elevation, and organic life. It thus made more sense, Humboldt claimed, to classify plants by climate zone instead of their taxonomy.

Humboldt's expedition to South America lasted about five years and included forays to Mexico, Cuba, and the United States, where he met President Thomas Jefferson, who had just dispatched the Lewis and Clark Expedition. It was, indeed, a great age of discovery.

---

1. To **oscillate** is to
a. waver
b. surrender
c. postpone
d. mitigate

2. If you **cavil** you
a. atone
b. deter
c. nitpick
d. memorialize

3. **Peremptory** logic is
a. self-effacing
b. unalloyed
c. irresolute
d. undeniable

4. The word **obtuse** most nearly means
a. acute
b. perceptive
c. dumb
d. nostalgic

5. A **luminous** career, such as Humbolt had, is
a. opaque
b. equivocal
c. murky
d. lustrous

6. The word **penitent** most nearly means
a. regretful
b. impoverished
c. extravagant
d. irrelevant

Read the following passage, taking note of the ***boldface*** *words and their contexts. These words are among those you will be studying in Unit 11. It may help you to complete the exercises in this Unit if you refer to the way the words are used below.*

Apollo 11 Poised for Take-Off

<Press Release>

For Immediate Release

Tomorrow, July 16, 1969, will mark the beginning of a bold new phase in humankind's **inexorable** quest to explore the universe. At approximately 9:30 a.m. EST, the Apollo 11 spacecraft will lift off from Cape Kennedy, Florida, for an eight-day, round-trip journey to the moon. The climax of this flight will come on July 20, when a manned lunar module will descend to the moon's surface. For the first time in history, humans will walk on another celestial body. The astronauts will explore the moon and gather rocks, dust, and other celestial **detritus** for analysis.

This mission represents the fulfillment of a universal dream. Throughout history, in every time and place, humans have stared at the moon and wondered. Wizards and **necromancers** of the past have claimed to have traveled to the moon, and storytellers and novelists have shared **delectable** tales of imaginary lunar adventures. In the past, these trips were, at best, mere flights of fancy. Today, in the shadow of the six-million-ton Saturn rocket poised for take-off, such imaginings pale and become **flaccid**, for America's astronauts will embark on a real adventure more gripping than any fiction.

The Apollo 11 mission is a response to a specific challenge. Eight years ago, President John F. Kennedy challenged the United States to land a man on the moon by the end of the decade. Such an achievement would require Americans to adopt a new and ambitious scientific outlook, discarding old and **moribund** attitudes. A few critics **deprecated** the President's challenge, saying the nation should focus on achievements closer to home. Others saw the task, rife with problems and danger, as too **onerous**. The program's expense also was at issue: Would the cost of a program culminating in a moon landing, estimated at some $25 billion, leave the United States **impecunious**? Despite these concerns and the **asperity** of the President's response to naysayers, the majority of Americans rose to the challenge, realizing that a lunar landing would open the door to "the last frontier." In spirit, the entire nation would be going to the moon along with its astronauts.

For its part, the National Aeronautics and Space Administration (NASA) has never considered **abrogating** its commitment to a lunar landing. By mastering the **rudiments** of manned space flight during the early Mercury and Gemini flights and by learning the lessons of recent Apollo missions, NASA scientists have developed a deep and **eclectic** set of aerospace engineering skills. These have enabled NASA to construct the most complex and sophisticated equipment on earth, and thanks to these tools the agency is **ebullient** about the prospects of tomorrow's extraordinary mission. The astronauts themselves—Neil Armstrong, Michael Collins, and Edwin "Buzz" Aldrin—are also cause for optimism. To select the three candidates, NASA **winnowed** a list of thousands of the country's best pilots and aeronautical engineers. Furthermore, these three men have undergone months of intense training for the upcoming mission, **burnishing** their considerable talents and skills. Tonight they are **sequestered** near the Florida launch site, confidently awaiting their chance to make history.

Although tomorrow's thunderous takeoff will begin a journey of more than 400,000 miles, it reminds us that even a journey of one thousand miles begins with a single step. Indeed, the Apollo 11 flight is but the beginning of a much longer voyage for humankind. The question of where our scientific explorations will take us—whether to Mars, to Venus, or to other solar systems—will not be answered for many years. Undoubtedly such destinations will be on future itineraries, but as tomorrow's launch reminds us, science's ultimate destination is limited only by mankind's knowledge, individual courage, and the forces of our expanding universe.

The Apollo 11 crew: Neil Armstrong, Michael Collins, Edwin "Buzz" Aldrin

Apollo 11 ready to take off

Audio

For iWords and audio passages, go to **SadlierConnect.com**.

Definitions

Note the spelling, pronunciation, part(s) of speech, and definition(s) of each of the following words. Then write the appropriate form of the word in the blank space in the illustrative sentence(s) following.

1. ambient (am′ bē ənt)
(*adj.*) completely surrounding, encompassing
The new filtering system is capable of cleaning and deodorizing the ________ air.

2. burnish (bər′ nish)
(*v.*) to make smooth or glossy by rubbing, polish; (*n.*) gloss, brightness, luster
The hotel manager ordered the waiters to ________ all the brass candlesticks before the formal banquet.
The ________ on the metal frame had faded with age and neglect.

3. cabal (kə bäl′)
(*n.*) a small group working in secret
The members of the ________ met at an unknown location for the purpose of fixing prices and stifling competition.

4. deprecate (dep′ rə kāt)
(*v.*) to express mild disapproval; to belittle
The administration ________ such foolish practices as the hazing of new students.

5. ebullient (i bül′ yənt)
(*adj.*) overflowing with enthusiasm and excitement; boiling, bubbling
After a string of very favorable reviews, the dance company was in an ________ mood for weeks.

6. eclectic (e klek′ tik)
(*adj.*) drawn from different sources; (*n.*) one whose beliefs are drawn from various sources
Stanford White developed an ________ style of architecture that made use of classic and modern elements.
The critics accused the composer of being a mere ________ with no original style of her own.

7. impecunious (im pə kyü′ nē əs)
(*adj.*) having little or no money
In my present ________ state, I will not be able to pay for dinner.

8. necromancer (nek′ rə man sər)
(*n.*) one who claims to reveal or influence the future through magic, especially communication with the dead; in general, a magician or wizard
When the stock market began to tumble, some desperate investors resorted to ________ for financial advice.

9. rife (rīf) (*adj.*) common, prevalent, widespread, happening often; full, abounding; plentiful, abundant, replete

Since rumors were ____________________, the president announced that the company had been bought out by its major competitor.

10. sequester (si kwes′ tər) (*v.*) to set apart, separate for a special purpose; to take possession of and hold in custody

The parties agreed to ____________________ the disputed funds pending a decision by the court.

Using Context

For each item, determine whether the ***boldface*** *word from pages 158–159 makes sense in the context of the sentence. Circle the item numbers next to the six sentences in which the words are used correctly.*

1. A tactful supervisor is one who can offer constructive feedback instead of harsh criticisms that **deprecate** an employee's work.
2. Perhaps the most famous **necromancer** in English literature is the wizard Merlin, a character who appears in the legend of King Arthur.
3. The body temperature of an ectothermic, or "cold-blooded," animal can fluctuate with the **ambient** temperature.
4. In the first act of *Macbeth*, three frightening-looking witches utter an eerie **cabal** over a large pot of boiling liquid.
5. The hit musical *Hamilton* tells the story of Alexander Hamilton's rise from **impecunious** orphan to first Secretary of the Treasury in a newly formed United States.
6. After writing *Harry Potter and the Sorcerer's Stone*, the author went on to **sequester** the story with six more novels about the young hero.
7. When I reread the email that I had sent to my teacher, I was shocked and embarrassed to see that it was **rife** with errors in spelling and punctuation.
8. Over time, moisture and salt air will **burnish** the paint on the beach house and cause it to peel.
9. The fans were **ebullient** when the referee ruled against their team and prevented the team from scoring.
10. The home features an **eclectic** collection of Asian, African, European, and Native American art.

Choosing the Right Word

*Select the **boldface** word that better completes each sentence. You might refer to the passage on pages 156–157 to see how most of these words are used in context. Note that the choices might be related forms of the Unit words.*

1. Oliver Wendell Holmes, Jr., once observed that he did not wish to lead a (**sequestered, burnished**) life far from the conflicts of his times.

2. As we sat in the locker room after our heartbreaking loss, the (**ambient, impecunious**) gloom was so thick you could almost cut it.

3. It is one thing to (**burnish, deprecate**) human follies and pretensions; it is quite another to correct them.

4. The charm of this musical comedy lies in its slam-bang pacing, its sprightly music, and its generally (**impecunious, ebullient**) good cheer.

5. (**Eclectic, Ambient**) schools of art are typical of a period when there is little original inspiration or bold experimentation.

6. Though she entered this country as a(n) (**impecunious, rife**) child, she eventually made a fortune in the garment industry.

7. "Did you use a cotton or a velvet cloth to (**burnish, sequester**) the antique mirror?" Bryan inquired.

8. (**Ebullience, Necromancy**) and other forms of witchcraft were punishable by death during the Middle Ages.

9. What appeared to be an informal study group was in reality a highly organized (**eclectic, cabal**) determined to overthrow the establishment.

10. The (**deprecated, burnished**) helmets and breastplates of the warriors gleamed and twinkled in the morning sunlight.

11. Any political party that is (**rife, ebullient**) with petty jealousies and backbiting can never hope to present a united front in an election.

12. The versatile actress was pronounced a(n) (**eclectic, necromancer**) for her work in many types of entertainment, though she mainly preferred theater.

Completing the Sentence

Choose the word from the word bank that best completes each of the following sentences. Write the correct word or form of the word in the space provided.

ambient	**cabal**	**ebullient**	**impecunious**	**rife**
burnish	**deprecate**	**eclectic**	**necromancer**	**sequester**

1. It was then that he began to organize the ________________ that would later depose the king.

2. The copper pots had been so highly ________________ that I could see my face in them.

3. The conversation at dinner tables all over town was ________________ with speculation as to the outcome of the big game.

4. In a sense, the woman is a(n) ________________ philosopher because her ideas have been influenced by many different schools of thought.

5. She is a very private person who ________________ any attempt to honor publicly her great services to humanity.

6. Some superstitious Roman emperors consulted ________________ and other dabblers in black magic to find out what the future held.

7. In order to prevent outside influences from coming into play, a jury is normally ________________ until it reaches a decision.

8. Even before they said a word, I could tell from their ________________ expressions that our team had won.

9. It is often difficult to hold a conversation while walking on a busy city street because of the high level of ________________ traffic noise.

10. The plot of the novel centers on a(n) ________________ adventurer who attempts to remedy his financial embarrassment by marrying into money.

End Set A

Definitions

Note the spelling, pronunciation, part(s) of speech, and definition(s) of each of the following words. Then write the appropriate form of the word in the blank space in the illustrative sentence(s) following.

1. abrogate (ab′ rə gāt)
(*v.*) to repeal, cancel, declare null and void
Often with no legal or moral grounds, the U.S. government would ____________________ treaties made with Native Americans.

2. asperity (a sper′ ə tē)
(*n.*) roughness, severity; bitterness or tartness
The ____________________ of the drama critic's statements undermined the young actor's confidence.

3. delectable (di lek′ tə bəl)
(*adj.*) delightful, highly enjoyable; deliciously flavored, savory; (*n.*) an appealing or appetizing food or dish
The banquet ended with a truly ____________________ dessert made of peaches, raspberries, and ice cream.
The eatery attracted customers with a mouth-watering display of ____________________ in its front window.

4. detritus (di trīt′ əs)
(*n.*) loose bits and pieces of material resulting from disintegration or wearing away; fragments that result from any destruction
Pieces of people's homes, furniture, and toys could be seen in the ____________________ of the landslide.

5. flaccid (flas′ əd)
(*adj.*) limp, not firm; lacking vigor or effectiveness
Because the injured bodybuilder had not worked out for weeks, his muscles grew ____________________.

6. inexorable (in ek′ sər ə bəl)
(*adj.*) inflexible, beyond influence; relentless, unyielding
In the Greek tragedies, nothing could save characters like Oedipus Rex from their ____________________ fates.

7. moribund (môr′ ə bənd)
(*adj.*) dying, on the way out
In the age of electronic communication, writing letters by hand seems to be a ____________________ custom.

8. onerous (än′ ər əs)
(*adj.*) burdensome; involving hardship or difficulty
Informing patients of bad news is an ____________________ duty that every doctor has to perform.

9. rudiments (rüd′ ə mənts)

(*n. pl.*) the parts of any subject or discipline that are learned first; the earliest stages of anything

At a very young age, the girl learned the ________________ of chess from her father, a professional player.

10. winnow (win′ ō)

(*v.*) to get rid of something unwanted, delete; to sift through to obtain what is desirable; to remove the chaff from the wheat by blowing air on it; to blow on, fan

Spelling and grammar software programs are designed to help writers ________________ inaccuracies from their documents.

Using Context

*For each item, determine whether the **boldface** word from pages 162–163 makes sense in the context of the sentence. Circle the item numbers next to the six sentences in which the words are used correctly.*

1. As an innkeeper she treats all her guests with hospitality and **asperity**.

2. He is known as an advertising genius whose **flaccid** ideas can build a strong marketing campaign for even the most mundane of products.

3. Although some people consider printed books to be **moribund** in the age of e-readers, I find nothing more satisfying than feeling the weight of a novel in my hands.

4. To become an expert in calculus, begin by mastering the **rudiments** of math.

5. When William Faulkner said, "In writing, you must kill your darlings," he meant that you should **winnow** any personally favorite words, phrases, or elements from your writing to avoid being repetitive.

6. I am lucky to have friends and family who always **abrogate** my ambitions, no matter how unattainable they may seem.

7. As she watched the crisp leaves fall off the trees and felt the first sting of the winter air, she lamented the **inexorable** changing of the seasons.

8. With my hectic schedule, nothing seems more **delectable** than a day with no responsibilities.

9. Construction on the brand-new building will begin soon, but first the crews have to clean up the **detritus** from the demolition of the old structure.

10. Mom was at first unhappy about taking the train to and from work, but now she finds it an **onerous** activity that allows her time to think, listen to music, and take in the scenery.

Choosing the Right Word

*Select the **boldface** word that better completes each sentence. You might refer to the passage on pages 156–157 to see how most of these words are used in context. Note that the choices might be related forms of the Unit words.*

1. As one veteran aptly observed, a soldier had to be hardy to cope with the (**asperities, detritus**) of life in the trenches during World War I.

2. Though skeptics insist that patriotism is (**onerous, moribund**) in America, I believe that it is alive and well in the hearts of the people.

3. Writing that is so full of soggy clichés, gummy sentence structure, and excessive wordiness can best be described as (**inexorable, flaccid**).

4. No one, however powerful or dominant, can (**abrogate, winnow**) the basic moral laws on which civilization rests.

5. Though the presidency confers great powers on the person who holds the office, it also saddles that person with (**onerous, flaccid**) responsibilities.

6. Despite our prodding, Aunt Eileen would not disclose the secret ingredient that makes her marinara sauce so (**delectable, inexorable**).

7. The investigating committee spent long hours trying to (**abrogate, winnow**) fact from fiction in the witnesses' testimony.

8. Since archaeologists spend a lot of time rummaging through the (**detritus, asperity**) of vanished civilizations, they bear a striking resemblance to junk collectors and ragpickers.

9. The film critic complained that some of the (**flaccid, inexorable**) tension in the original film has been lost in this year's milder remake.

10. The old adage that "one man's meat is another man's poison" simply means that what is considered (**delectable, onerous**) is often quite subjective.

11. Anyone who has the slightest acquaintance with the (**rudiments, delectables**) of economic theory understands that we cannot solve our financial problems simply by borrowing more and more money.

12. "The (**inexorable, moribund**) march of the years," said the aged speaker, "decrees that this is the last time I will address you."

Completing the Sentence

Choose the word from the word bank that best completes each of the following sentences. Write the correct word or form of the word in the spaces provided.

abrogate	**delectable**	**flaccid**	**moribund**	**rudiments**
asperity	**detritus**	**inexorable**	**onerous**	**winnow**

1. We will never allow anyone to curtail or ____________________ the basic rights and liberties guaranteed to us in the Constitution.

2. Though monarchies still exist in some parts of the world, they are more or less a(n) ____________________ form of government.

3. I thought the job of revising the manuscript would be a relatively simple matter, but it proved to be a(n) ____________________ task.

4. Unless you have mastered the ____________________ of French grammar, you will find it difficult to speak the language fluently.

5. I could tell that my boss was really "riled" by the ____________________ of his tone of voice when he summoned me.

6. All the facts and figures point to one ____________________ conclusion: we are hopelessly outnumbered.

7. One of Darwin's theories suggests that nature ensures the survival of a species by slowly ____________________ out the less fit members.

8. Late that night, we began the heartbreaking task of sifting through the ____________________ of our ravaged home.

9. There is nothing more ____________________ on a hot day than to stretch out in a hammock with a good book and pitcher of icy lemonade!

10. As air slowly seeped out through the tiny puncture, the inner tube became more and more ____________________.

End Set B

Synonyms

*Choose the word or form of the word from this Unit that is the same or most nearly the same in meaning as the **boldface** word or expression in the phrase. Write that word on the line. Use a dictionary if necessary.*

1. a garden **filled** with weeds ______________
2. the **conjurer's** magic tricks ______________
3. the **exuberant** cheerleading squad ______________
4. noticed another **fading** tradition ______________
5. the **harshness** of the coach's rant ______________
6. rebelled against the **oppressive** taxation ______________
7. **diffusive** smells in the air ______________
8. **reduce** the list of players ______________
9. sheltered the **penniless** immigrants ______________
10. a **varied collection** of opinions ______________
11. cleaned up the **debris** from the parade ______________
12. study the **fundamentals** of grammar ______________
13. the **inescapable** consequences of her actions ______________
14. **secluded** on a remote country estate ______________
15. a ruthless **clique** of gangsters ______________

Antonyms

*Choose the word or form of the word from this Unit that is most nearly opposite in meaning to the **boldface** word or expression in the phrase. Write that word on the line. Use a dictionary if necessary.*

1. a cleaning agent that **abraded** his new sports car ______________
2. will **reaffirm** his oath to the king ______________
3. noticed her **firm** handshake ______________
4. **countenanced** our peaceful protest ______________
5. a **repulsive** meal ______________

Writing: Words in Action

If you were offered the opportunity, would you like to be a passenger on a space flight to the moon? Why or why not? In a short essay, explain your position. Use examples from your reading (pages 156–157), studies, and personal observations. Use three or more words from this Unit to support your position.

Vocabulary in Context

*Some of the words you have studied in this Unit appear in **boldface** type. Read the passage below, and then circle the letter of the correct answer for each word as it is used in context.*

European Space Agency scientists were **ebullient** when their spacecraft Rosetta completed its 4-billion-mile journey through the solar system and pulled alongside Comet 67P/Churyumov-Gerasimenko. The goal of the mission was to study the composition of the comet as it swung around the sun. Since comets are "leftovers" from the formation of the solar system around 4.6 billion years ago, they are likely to hold important clues about Earth's history, including the origin of life. Like other comets, Comet 67P is **rife** with water—in its frozen form—and some scientists theorize that Earth got much of its water from a bombardment of asteroids and comets several hundred million years after the planet's formation.

A key part of the Rosetta mission was its robotic lander, Philae. Never before had a spacecraft landed on a comet, and the 220-pound craft carried an array of instruments to analyze the alien surface. Because the comet has little gravity, Philae needed to fire a thruster to hold it against the comet's surface, thus giving it time to shoot "harpoons" that would anchor it there. Unfortunately, the thruster failed, and Philae bounced a couple of times before coming to rest near a cliff, where **ambient** shade prevented its solar panels from recharging its batteries. The little lander was essentially **moribund**. So scientists quickly put it to work—drilling, sampling, and transmitting data back to Rosetta—before it used up its 60 hours of original battery life.

Scientists must now **winnow** the vast amount of information collected by Rosetta and Philae. Anything but a **cabal**, Rosetta's team has been a model of openness, regularly communicating its findings with other scientists and the public. Many important papers about the role of comets in the early solar system are anticipated.

---

1. **Ebullient** scientists are
a. satisfied **c.** anxious
b. proud **d.** very excited

2. The word **rife** most nearly means
a. scarce **c.** abundant
b. flooded **d.** possible

3. **Ambient** shade is
a. dark **c.** perpetual
b. natural **d.** encompassing

4. If a lander is **moribund**, it is
a. dying **c.** expired
b. not working **d.** faulty

5. When scientists **winnow** information, they
a. organize it **c.** analyze it
b. sift through it **d.** put it in order

6. A **cabal** is a(n)
a. secret group **c.** team of scientists
b. international body **d.** private university

*Read the following passage, taking note of the **boldface** words and their contexts. These words are among those you will be studying in Unit 12. It may help you to complete the exercises in this Unit if you refer to the way the words are used below.*

Pyramids: Monuments to Gods and Men

<Compare and Contrast Essay>

Imposing, mysterious pyramids, found in areas from Asia to the Middle East to South America, have fascinated people for millennia. Some pyramids are lauded for their **aesthetic** qualities; some, though not as beautiful, are equally intriguing. Who built these architectural wonders? Why were they built, and what is their significance? And how were they built, given the technological limitations?

The world's largest pyramids are in Egypt, in the Valley of the Kings, near Cairo, and in Teotihuacan, in proximity to Mexico City, where these massive constructions seem **omnipresent** and command the attention of all onlookers. The two pyramids were built for different reasons—as tombs for Egypt's pharaohs and as places of worship and ritual for the Teotihuacans, but **impeccable** planning went into the erecting of each.

The Great Pyramid of Giza (also known as the Great Pyramid of Khufu, or Cheops) was one of the Seven Wonders of the Ancient World. It was constructed circa 2560 B.C. and is made up of 2.3 million limestone blocks. Estimates vary, but it took perhaps 30,000 men 20 years to complete the first Great Pyramid and its remarkable complex of secret chambers and hidden passages. It was created as a tomb for Pharaoh Khufu, who **espoused** a belief in the afterlife and wanted a resting place for himself, his wives, and his treasures within a structure that would thwart and **discomfit** his enemies. Nearby, as part of the Giza Necropolis, are another two pyramids and the Great Sphinx.

Ancient artifacts have been uncovered from the pyramids and other monuments in Giza, Egypt.

All have withstood the natural elements: As an old proverb says, the pyramids mock time.

Unlike Egyptian pyramids, Mesoamerican pyramids are typically step pyramids with a temple at the peak. The three magnificent pyramids of Teotihuacan—the Pyramid of the Moon, the Pyramid of the Sun and the Feathered Serpent Pyramid—are part of a massive archaeological site in the Basin of Mexico. The main street, the "Avenue of the Dead," is lined with smaller temples and residences, and excavations throughout the site have turned up fertility **fetishes** and other talismans. The largest structure, the Pyramid of the Sun, was completed by A.D. 100 and is about half as tall as the Great Pyramid of Giza. The pyramid's core was mainly volcanic ash and gravel, while a thick layer of stone and mortar made up its walls. Incredibly, the builders were able to erect these marvels without the aid of the wheel or metal tools.

The early history of Teotihuacan is enigmatic because no one is completely sure which ancient, **gregarious** society built North America's first great city. The inhabitants used the pyramids in their religious rites and sacrifices. Ignoring the **plaintive** wails of their **hapless** victims, they **importuned** the gods for favors. The city's **nadir** came about A.D. 600, when the Teotihuacans abandoned their home, but a later Indian civilization, the Aztecs, adopted the city and kept it from becoming **defunct**. They dubbed the place the "City of the Gods," or "Place Where Men Become Gods."

Over time, explorers and treasure hunters have done lasting and **irreparable** damage to the world's pyramids, including those in Egypt and Teotihuacan. In many cases, authorities have made inferior, **perfunctory** repairs or allowed the damaged pyramids to **languish** and fall into disrepair, but now both sites are protected as national treasures by their governments. Thousands of tourists visit the pyramids in the Valley of the Kings and Teotihuacan every year.

Audio

For iWords and audio passages, go to **SadlierConnect.com**.

Ceramics such as this seated figure were found at Teotihuacan in Mexico.

Definitions

Note the spelling, pronunciation, part(s) of speech, and definition(s) of each of the following words. Then write the appropriate form of the word in the blank space in the illustrative sentence(s) following.

1. discomfit (dis kəm′ fit)
(*v.*) to frustrate, thwart, or defeat; to confuse, perplex, or embarrass
The general tried to ____________ his enemies by repeatedly beginning an advance and then pulling back.

2. gregarious (grə gār′ ē əs)
(*adj.*) living together in a herd or group; sociable, seeking the company of others
I would expect the recreation director of a cruise ship to be a ____________ person.

3. hapless (hap′ lis)
(*adj.*) marked by a persistent absence of good luck
Once again, my younger brother has become the ____________ victim of a silly practical joke.

4. importune (im pôr tyün′)
(*v.*) to trouble with demands; to beg for insistently
My bankrupt uncle ____________ my father for a loan.

5. irreparable (i rep′ ər ə bəl)
(*adj.*) incapable of being repaired or rectified
The husband believed that the surgeon did ____________ harm to his wife and sued the doctor and the hospital.

6. laconic (lə kän′ ik)
(*adj.*) concise, using few words
The senator issued a ____________ statement declaring her innocence after the accusations of fraud were made public.

7. languish (laŋ′ gwish)
(*v.*) to become weak, feeble, or dull; to droop; to be depressed or dispirited; to suffer neglect
Without the constitutional guarantee of a speedy trial, the accused could ____________ in jail for years.

8. omnipresent (äm ni pre′ zənt)
(*adj.*) present in all places at all times
They believed in an ____________ deity that existed in all things.

9. plaintive (plān′ tiv) (*adj.*) expressive of sorrow or woe, melancholy

The recently widowed man spoke of his loneliness in a ____________________ tone of voice.

10. tantamount (tan′ tə mau̇nt) (*adj.*) equivalent, having the same meaning, value, or effect

The armed invasion of their territory was ____________________ to a declaration of war.

Using Context

*For each item, determine whether the **boldface** word from pages 170–171 makes sense in the context of the sentence. Circle the item numbers next to the six sentences in which the words are used correctly.*

1. The insurance company issued a check to cover the cost of replacing the vehicle once it was determined that the damage to the car was **irreparable**.

2. Her various objections to our plan, many of them unfounded, seemed to be attempts to **discomfit** us rather than legitimate concerns.

3. The lettuce, kale, arugula, and basil that we planted in the garden will **languish** in this oppressive heat wave.

4. When you reread and edit your essay, be sure to look for **gregarious** ideas and details that should be deleted.

5. Charlie Brown, who is featured in the comic strip Peanuts, is a classic **hapless** character; nothing he does ever seems to turn out right.

6. The software company will **importune** a new version of its best-selling photo editing program by the end of this year.

7. In the weeks before the election, signs and posters promoting the major candidates were **omnipresent**.

8. Do you prefer soft, muted colors or bright, **plaintive** ones?

9. The **laconic** melody of the Appalachian folk song brings tears to my eyes every time I hear it.

10. Rightly or wrongly, many people interpreted the mayor's refusal to answer questions about the charges of corruption as **tantamount** to an admission of guilt.

Choosing the Right Word

*Select the **boldface** word that better completes each sentence. You might refer to the passage on pages 168–169 to see how most of these words are used in context. Note that the choices might be related forms of the Unit words.*

1. One of the best-known figures of American folklore is the lean, tough, (**laconic, hapless**) cowboy.

2. Though I left the house feeling "as fit as a fiddle," my spirits began to (**importune, languish**) after only five minutes in that withering heat.

3. The legal adage "Silence implies consent" means that not objecting to an action that concerns you is (**omnipresent, tantamount**) to approving it.

4. The whiny toddler (**importuned, discomfited**) his mother for a snack.

5. She sang a (**laconic, plaintive**) little ditty about a man who yearns wistfully for the girl he left behind many years before.

6. The (**omnipresent, gregarious**) threat of a nuclear holocaust that characterized the Cold War era changed many people's attitudes toward war in profound ways.

7. When the scandal broke, the man found himself the (**hapless, plaintive**) victim of other people's misdeeds.

8. The sternness of my boss's expression so (**discomfited, languished**) me that at first I had difficulty responding to the question.

9. A diplomat must always proceed on the assumption that no rupture between nations, no matter how serious, is (**irreparable, tantamount**).

10. I don't know which is more painful—to have to ask someone for a favor or to have some unfortunate (**importune, discomfit**) one for help.

11. After the death of his wife of seven decades, a grieving Mr. Johnson (**languished, importuned**) in their quiet apartment.

12. Prehistoric peoples banded together into tribes, not only for protection, but also to satisfy their (**gregarious, irreparable**) instincts.

Completing the Sentence

Choose the word from the word bank that best completes each of the following sentences. Write the correct word or form of the word in the space provided.

discomfit	**hapless**	**irreparable**	**languish**	**plaintive**
gregarious	**importune**	**laconic**	**omnipresent**	**tantamount**

1. Suddenly I was surrounded by a mob of street urchins loudly ____________ me for a handout.

2. Last night, Central High's Shooting Stars captured the basketball championship by ____________ the South High Slammers, 61 to 44.

3. When asked what terms he would offer the Confederate army, General Grant made the ____________ reply, "Unconditional surrender!"

4. No matter where candidates for high political office go these days, the ____________ eye of the TV camera seems focused on them.

5. Since extroverts are ____________ by nature, they usually prefer not to live alone.

6. The ____________ creature had somehow gotten its foot caught in the grate and could not extricate it without help.

7. When you get more experience on the job, you will learn that a "request" from your employer is ____________ to an order.

8. Responding to the melancholy note in the song of the nightingale, Keats wrote of its "____________ anthem."

9. I was greatly relieved to learn that the accident I had with my car last week didn't do any ____________ damage to the motor.

10. I thought our state legislators would consider the proposal at the earliest opportunity, but they let it ____________ in committee for months.

End Set A

Definitions

Note the spelling, pronunciation, part(s) of speech, and definition(s) of each of the following words. Then write the appropriate form of the word in the blank space in the illustrative sentence(s) following.

1. aesthetic (es thet′ ik)

(*adj.*) pertaining to beauty; sensitive or responsive to beauty

Since the structure had no practical purpose, keeping it in place could only be justified on ____________ grounds.

2. defunct (di fəŋkt′)

(*adj.*) no longer in existence or functioning, dead

I could find no forwarding address or phone number for the ____________ organization.

3. espouse (es paüz′)

(*v.*) to take up and support; to become attached to, adopt; to marry

To appeal to the large number of dissatisfied voters, the candidate ____________ a strong program of reform.

4. fetish (fet′ ish)

(*n.*) an object believed to have magical powers; an object of unreasoning devotion or reverence

The rabbit's foot, once a very popular ____________, seems to have lost its hold on the public imagination.

5. impeccable (im pek′ ə bəl)

(*adj.*) faultless, beyond criticism or blame

We always consulted my grandmother about what to wear because she had ____________ taste in clothing.

6. interpolate (in tər′ pə lāt)

(*v.*) to insert between other parts or things; to present as an addition or correction

At the director's request, the screenwriter ____________ some new lines into the script.

7. mendacious (men dā′ shəs)

(*adj.*) given to lying or deception; untrue

The deputy gave a ____________ account of his employer's actions on the day of the alleged crime.

8. nadir (nā′ dər)

(*n.*) the lowest point

At the ____________ of his popularity, the prime minister decided to resign his office and call for new elections.

9. perfunctory (per fəŋk′ tə rē) (*adj.*) done in a superficial or halfhearted manner; without interest or enthusiasm

The police made a ________________ search for the missing handbag, but they really did not expect to find it.

10. requite (ri kwīt′) (*v.*) to make suitable repayment, as for a kindness, service, or favor; to make retaliation, as for an injury or wrong; to reciprocate

We made sure to ________________ the neighbors for looking after our house while we were away.

Using Context

*For each item, determine whether the **boldface** word from pages 174–175 makes sense in the context of the sentence. Circle the item numbers next to the six sentences in which the words are used correctly.*

1. The reporter's invention of some facts and failure to verify others resulted in a **mendacious** report and led to her dismissal from the staff.
2. Because that chapter has a different tone and style from the rest of the book, many people believe that the author decided to **interpolate** it into the novel as an afterthought.
3. The chess club is now **defunct** because no one took the job of managing it after I left.
4. By the end of a long week, I was in such a state of **nadir** that I fell asleep as soon as my head hit the pillow.
5. You can go ahead and throw away that stuffed toy because the child now sees it as nothing but a **fetish**.
6. When I asked if he had seen my twenty-dollar bill, he made only a **perfunctory** glance around the room before answering no, so I suspected he did not take a serious look.
7. Her Spanish is so **impeccable** that Spaniards mistake her for a native when she travels abroad.
8. Now that they are parents of teenagers, the couple does not **espouse** the childrearing views held by their friends, who have younger children.
9. Although the custom seems outdated, the restaurant will **requite** that you wear a jacket if you come for dinner.
10. That polluted lake, surrounded by those litter-filled, marshy grounds, has a strong **aesthetic** quality.

Choosing the Right Word

*Select the **boldface** word that better completes each sentence. You might refer to the passage on pages 168–169 to see how most of these words are used in context. Note that the choices might be related forms of the Unit words.*

1. In the *Poetics* and the *Metaphysics*, Greek philosopher Aristotle discusses the purpose of art and identifies important (**defunct, aesthetic**) principles.

2. Fortunately, our lawyer was able to produce documents that disproved the (**mendacious, impeccable**) assertions of our former partner.

3. One of the comforting things about reaching the (**fetish, nadir**) of one's career is that the only place to go from there is up.

4. Her sense of tact is so (**aesthetic, impeccable**) and unerring that she can handle the most trying situation as if it were mere child's play.

5. I hope to (**espouse, requite**) my parents for all the care they have shown me.

6. Faced with a tight deadline, the exhausted editor gave the young reporter's article a hurried and (**perfunctory, mendacious**) edit.

7. Though few of us today stand on ceremony to quite the extent that our ancestors did, common courtesy is by no means (**impeccable, defunct**).

8. Many scholars believe that Beaumont or Fletcher (**interpolated, requited**) a scene or two into the present text of Shakespeare's *Macbeth*.

9. Perhaps we should be overjoyed that the great man condescended to give us a(n) (**aesthetic, perfunctory**) nod as we passed by.

10. In our desire to improve the quality of life in America, we should not be too quick to (**interpolate, espouse**) an idea simply because it is new.

11. It is one thing to be concerned about discipline; it is quite another to make a (**nadir, fetish**) of it.

12. "Despite taking an oath to tell the truth, Laurie offered clearly (**perfunctory, mendacious**) testimony," complained the frustrated defense attorney.

Completing the Sentence

Choose the word from the word bank that best completes each of the following sentences. Write the correct word or form of the word in the space provided.

aesthetic	**espouse**	**impeccable**	**mendacious**	**perfunctory**
defunct	**fetish**	**interpolate**	**nadir**	**requite**

1. One wall of the museum was filled with charms and ______________________ designed to ward off everything from a hangnail to the evil eye.

2. As his irrepressible flow of reminiscences continued without a letup, I tried in vain to ______________________ a few observations of my own.

3. Every general seems to have one defeat that marks the ______________________ of his military fortunes—for example, Lee at Gettysburg or Grant at Cold Harbor.

4. It's easy enough to back a popular program, but it takes real courage to ______________________ a cause that most people oppose.

5. Never once has the least whiff of a scandal or impropriety tainted the man's ______________________ reputation as an upstanding member of this agency.

6. I felt a little foolish when the librarian told me that I was asking for the current issue of a magazine that had long been ______________________.

7. "Don't you think it's a little foolish to pursue the young lady when your warm feelings for her are clearly not ______________________?" I asked.

8. To say that he is ______________________ does not even begin to convey just how alienated he is from any regard for the truth.

9. They claim to have made a thorough search of the premises, but I suspect that their efforts were no more than ______________________.

10. From a(n) ______________________ point of view, the painting didn't appeal to me, but I kept it because it was a memento of my childhood.

End Set B

Synonyms

*Choose the word or form of the word from this Unit that is the same or most nearly the same in meaning as the **boldface** word or expression in the phrase. Write that word on the line. Use a dictionary if necessary.*

1. wears a **charm** on her necklace ____________
2. kept repeating that **doleful** melody ____________
3. listened to a **terse** summary ____________
4. a **ubiquitous** presence ____________
5. **entreated** the governor for a pardon ____________
6. **embraced** the cause of equality ____________
7. cautioned me against the **dishonest** salesperson ____________
8. **recompensed** them for their hospitality ____________
9. **disconcerted** the conservative audience ____________
10. made **artistic** improvements ____________
11. **wilt** under the hot sun ____________
12. did **irreversible** damage ____________
13. no more than a **cursory** note of apology ____________
14. tried to **interject** a different opinion ____________
15. **equal** to betraying a friend ____________

Antonyms

*Choose the word or form of the word from this Unit that is most nearly opposite in meaning to the **boldface** word or expression in the phrase. Write that word on the line. Use a dictionary if necessary.*

1. the restaurant's **flawed** service ____________
2. the **pinnacle** of company morale ____________
3. lived a **charmed** existence ____________
4. the **existing** government ____________
5. had an **introverted** nature ____________

Writing: Words in Action

How important is it for high school students to study world history—to learn, for example, about the ancient civilizations of Egypt and Teotihuacan? In a brief essay, explain your opinion with examples from your reading (refer to pages 168–169), experiences, or current events. Use three or more words from this Unit.

Vocabulary in Context

*Some of the words you have studied in this Unit appear in **boldface** type. Read the passage below, and then circle the letter of the correct answer for each word as it is used in context.*

The mystery of who built the Egyptian pyramids has been under debate ever since Greek historian Herodotus made a **laconic** claim that 100,000 enslaved workers built the Great Pyramid. However, graffiti discovered inside the Giza monuments proves that version of history to be **mendacious**. Modern-day Egyptologists **interpolate** a new theory about who built the pyramids. They now believe that approximately 4,000 quarry workers, haulers, and masons lived in Giza and worked on the pyramids year-round. During the late summer and early fall, a crew of approximately 20,000 ramp builders, tool-makers, and mortar mixers arrived at the **nadir** of Giza to help build these monuments to the afterlife for their pharaohs. These workers, who labored for 20 years, believed that the afterlife would **requite** them for their work on these pyramids.

There was a hierarchy among these workers—approximately 5,000 permanent workers earned a salary and lived with their families in a well-appointed pyramid village, and up to 20,000 temporary workers lived in less elaborate accommodations adjacent to the pyramid village. This lodging for temporary workers was **tantamount** to a campsite, and they were paid for their work with 10 loaves of bread and a beverage—just enough to feed a family for a day. The temporary workers may have even been subject to the pharaoh's compulsory labor system that required inhabitants to work for three to four months on state projects. By discovering that permanent workers were paid and that the workers who were not compensated monetarily were temporary workers, Egyptologists disproved a popular myth about who really built the pyramids.

---

1. If you are **laconic**, you are
a. unreasonable **c.** deliberate
b. relaxed **d.** concise

2. A **mendacious** version of history is
a. untrue **c.** superficial
b. unrealistic **d.** exaggerated

3. The word **interpolate** most nearly means
a. connect **c.** introduce
b. infer **d.** illustrate

4. A **nadir** is
a. the general vicinity **c.** the pinnacle
b. the lowest point **d.** the entrance

5. To **requite** is to
a. pay back **c.** perform a duty
b. instruct **d.** receive money

6. The word **tantamount** most nearly means
a. adjacent **c.** equivalent
b. dissimilar **d.** unrelated

Vocabulary for Comprehension

Part 1

*Read this passage, which contains words in **boldface** that appear in Units 10–12. Then choose the best answer to each question based on what is stated or implied in the passage. You may refer to the passage as often as necessary.*

Questions 1–10 are based on the following passage.

While not many Englishmen followed the example of Thomas Paine by joining the insurrection in the American colonies, it would be a mistake to think that Paine left behind him a country **obsequious** in its support for King George III. Some of Britain's most widely read newspapers had long supported the disaffected colonists. When armed resistance broke out in 1775 in Massachusetts, the *Westminster Chronicle* referred to the revolutionaries as Britain's "brethren." The *Scots Magazine* gave this **laconic** description of George Washington: "a man of sense and great integrity."

The colonists' rallying cry of "No taxation without representation" was understood very clearly in several of Britain's major cities. The House of Commons was an elected body, but it was chronically unrepresentative. Its members mostly represented small towns and rural areas. The Industrial Revolution was creating enormous new cities rife with factory workers—unbelievably, Manchester and Birmingham had no more parliamentary representation than the American colonies. Populations without parliamentary representation in the industrial north and midlands of Britain felt a profound connection, **tantamount** to kinship, with their revolutionary brethren in America.

Not everyone in England was against taxation without representation, even though it was more a matter of legality than principle. The law was clearly on the side of the framers of the Declaration of Rights drafted by the First Continental Congress (1774). Samuel Johnson wrote *Taxation No Tyranny* in 1775 in response. He claimed that by emigrating, colonists had "voluntarily resigned the power of voting," and **deprecated** as traitors Englishmen who **espoused** the American cause. Johnson's **asperity**, however, was complicated by his attitude to colonialism. In 1756, during the French and Indian War, he had described the British and the French as "two robbers" fighting over North American lands they had stolen from "the natural lords and original inhabitants." His hope that the problem would be solved by "English superiority and American obedience" indicates a belief shared by most in England, except Thomas Paine, that war was avoidable.

The outbreak of war took England by surprise and nobody was more surprised than the reliably **obtuse** George III. His address to Parliament on October 31, 1776 betrays the **foible** of his failure to acknowledge the sincerity of American efforts to remain loyal British subjects, and the goodwill that characterized their faith in British law. They appealed with heroic persistence for the justice due to colonial citizens: "They meant only to amuse by vague expressions of attachment to the Parent State, and the strongest protestations of loyalty to me, whilst they were preparing for a general revolt."

Addressing Parliament a year later, the **hapless** monarch expressed astonishment at the sheer ingratitude of his American colonies—an astonishment nourished by self-delusion. "No people," he said, "ever enjoyed more Happiness, or lived under a milder Government, than those now revolted Provinces: the Improvements in every Art, of which they boast, declare it: their Numbers, their Wealth, their Strength by Sea and Land, which they think sufficient to enable them to make Head against the whole Power of the Mother Country, are irrefragable Proofs of it."

1. The primary purpose of the passage is to
A) indicate the diversity of British attitudes to the American colonists as disaffection developed into revolutionary commitment.
B) suggest that the British people were not to blame for the errors of their king.
C) show how King George III was to blame for losing the American colonies.
D) demonstrate that opinions can change in response to political developments.

2. Which choice best summarizes the second paragraph (lines 16–32)?
A) Disaffected American colonists gained support among the non-enfranchised populations of British industrial cities.
B) The British had a total lack of parliamentary representation.
C) American colonists visited cities in the industrial north and midlands of Britain.
D) Britain's industrial cities adopted cry of "No taxation without representation."

3. As it is used in line 43, "deprecated" most nearly means
A) described.
B) dismissed.
C) condemned.
D) commended.

4. As it is used in line 44, "espoused" most nearly means
A) opposed.
B) disavowed.
C) embraced.
D) fought for.

5. It can reasonably be inferred from the third paragraph (lines 33–56) that Johnson
A) was by nature a patriot.
B) wanted to use force on the colonies.
C) supported the rights of American Indians.
D) was a British imperialist.

6. Which choice provides the best evidence for the answer to the previous question?
A) Lines 41–43 ("He claimed…traitors")
B) Lines 45–46 ("Johnson's … colonialism")
C) Lines 47–52 ("In 1756… inhabitants")
D) Lines 53–56 ("English...avoidable")

7. According to the passage, the American revolutionaries
A) were first-generation British immigrants.
B) embraced taxation.
C) relied on the support of the British press.
D) were loyal subjects driven to extreme measures by British inflexibility.

8. It can reasonably be inferred from the fourth paragraph (lines 57–71) that
A) King George had never believed in the loyalty of his colonial subjects.
B) the author sympathizes with the colonists.
C) loyal British subjects had been corrupted by foreign influences.
D) the author sympathizes with the king.

9. As it is used in line 73, "hapless" most nearly means
A) wretched.
B) inopportune.
C) ill-advised.
D) unpopular.

10. What point does the author make by including the last paragraph?
A) The king was mistaken about his relationship with the colonies.
B) The king regretted the American colonialists' need for self-government.
C) The king was afraid the American colonists were going to defeat Britain.
D) The king would never spoil any other colonies with gifts that had made America so disobedient and ungrateful.

Vocabulary for Comprehension Part 2

Read these passages, which contain words in ***boldface*** *that appear in Units 10–12. Then choose the best answer to each question based on what is stated or implied in the passage(s). You may refer to the passages as often as necessary.*

Questions 1–10 are based on the following passages.

Passage 1

For centuries, quarantine, or isolation of infected individuals, was a common response to infectious disease outbreaks. Quarantine was used in the fourteenth century to **attenuate** the spread of bubonic plague. Infected individuals were confined, but entire towns were also **peremptorily** quarantined. Quarantine generally lasted 40 days for those the disease didn't **decimate,** and an eventual decrease in plague cases seemed to confirm quarantine's effectiveness, and so it was used in the eighteenth century when cholera was **rife** in Europe.

Recently, quarantine has faced criticism. First, its efficacy was questioned, as people fleeing the quarantine spread the disease in **ambient** areas. Also, human rights concerns arose about discrimination against people suspected of being infected and the violation of personal rights of people affected by general quarantine. Health organizations are increasingly **espousing** contact tracing to control infectious disease, a method in which health workers find individuals who have had contact with an infected person. The contact is monitored for signs of disease. If the contact is disease free, he or she is no longer monitored. Contact tracing leads to many non-infected people being monitored and isolated, but that number is smaller than under general quarantine.

Passage 2

In December 2013, the number of new cases of Ebola virus disease (EVD), a hemorrhagic fever, reported in West Africa concerned the international medical community. The virus spread with unprecedented and **inexorable** rapidity through three of the poorest and most politically unstable nations on Earth. On August 8, 2014, when morale was at its **nadir**, the World Health Organization (WHO) declared the Ebola epidemic a public health emergency of international concern (PHEIC). The director-general gave warning of the global catastrophe that would undoubtedly occur if the epidemic were not **rebuffed** before it spread. Teams of doctors, nurses, and trained ancillaries arrived from all over the world. The International Federation for Emergency Medicine created emergency aid initiatives and training programs for medical staff enlisted from local communities.

Quarantine is impractical in environments like these, and variable incubation periods reduce the effectiveness of selecting and **sequestering** groups of people. Community engagement and education were the first steps to halting the epidemic in West Africa. The use of contact tracing was used to halt Ebola. Individual case management and social mobilization created the trust necessary for the tracing and effective surveillance of people who had contact with an infected person.

Of the 28,616 Ebola cases that were reported; 10,000 people survived. On March 29, 2016, the WHO declared the emergency **moribund.**

1. The primary purpose of Passage 1 is to
A) make readers aware of the dangers of infectious disease throughout the world.
B) briefly describe changes in the medical response to infectious disease.
C) make an argument for the use of quarantine in containing epidemics.
D) describe the conditions that give rise to outbreaks of infectious disease.

2. As it is used in line 5, “attenuate” most nearly means
A) to warn against.
B) to halt completely.
C) to lessen in force.
D) to assist in.

3. As it is used in line 14, “rife” most nearly means
A) prevalent.
B) emerging.
C) declining.
D) epidemic.

4. As it is used in line 39, “inexorable” most nearly means
A) unprecedented.
B) unpredictable.
C) relentless.
D) beatable.

5. As it is used in line 43, “nadir” most nearly means
A) climax.
B) lowest point.
C) epicenter.
D) highest point.

6. It can reasonably be inferred from Passage 2 that Ebola
A) is curable and no longer a problem.
B) will continue to spread.
C) is incurable and almost always fatal.
D) may be contained and treated.

7. In Passage 1, the author describes diseases that affected entire continents, while in Passage 2, the author stresses
A) that finding a cure for the Ebola virus is a community concern.
B) that local disease outbreaks can now become worldwide disasters.
C) the importance of isolating small communities affected by an epidemic.
D) the necessity of keeping the global community calm and informed.

8. Which choice provides the best evidence for the answer to the previous question?
A) Lines 46–49 (“The director-general . . . spread”)
B) Lines 49–51 (“Teams. . . world”)
C) Lines 51–55 (“The . . . communities”)
D) Lines 56–59 (“Quarantine. . . people”)

9. How would the author of Passage 1 most likely respond to the medical community’s methods described in lines 56–67 of Passage 2?
A) The author would agree that contact tracing was the best approach.
B) The author would recommend contact tracing and quarantine to halt Ebola.
C) The author would raise concerns about human rights violations.
D) The author would argue that the number of people affected by Ebola in West Africa made contact tracing impossible.

10. Which statement describes the relationship between Passage 1 and Passage 2?
A) Both passages argue that international cooperation is necessary.
B) Both passages make the point that quarantine is effective.
C) Passage 1 argues for the use of quarantine, and Passage 2 argues for the use of contact tracing.
D) Passage 1 describes the methods to contain epidemics, and Passage 2 describes a real-world use of a new method to contain an epidemic.

Synonyms

*From the word bank below, choose the word that has the same or nearly the same meaning as the **boldface** word in each sentence and write it on the line. You will not use all of the words.*

delectable	**inexorable**	**nadir**	**perfunctory**
ebullient	**irreparable**	**omnipresent**	**reconnoiter**
fraught	**languish**	**oscillate**	**rife**
gregarious	**luminous**	**peremptory**	**winnow**

1. You didn't truly clean and organize; instead you did a **slapdash** job of putting the clutter out of sight. ______________________
2. I appreciate the librarian's **outgoing** personality, but I wish he wouldn't make conversation with me while I'm studying. ______________________
3. Even though there's still a lot of work to do, you will begin to **weaken** if you don't take time to rest and have a decent meal. ______________________
4. Before she said a word, we could tell from her **elated** expression that she had finally gotten a promotion. ______________________
5. Nothing had ever tasted more **scrumptious** than a home-cooked meal after a week of subsisting on canned food while camping. ______________________
6. After the biting insult, the silence in the room was **charged** with tension as we waited for the other person's response. ______________________
7. Although the accident hadn't seemed too bad, the damage to the vehicle was **irremediable** and I needed to buy a new car. ______________________
8. The **refulgent** sunlight that streamed through the clouds after the rain immediately brightened his mood. ______________________
9. In the last weeks of the school year, the hallways were **replete** with excitement for the approaching summer. ______________________
10. Before the big game, the athletes tried to **scout** the team they would play the next day to identify their strategies. ______________________
11. In the focus group, we try to **filter** out any people who might have preconceived notions about the product we're testing. ______________________
12. Despite my wish for the crisp fall weather to last forever, winter made its **obdurate** presence known by dumping a snowstorm in the middle of November. ______________________

Two-Word Completions

Select the pair of words that best completes the meaning of each of the following sentences.

1. Though the man appeared to be the most ________________ pauper on the face of the earth, he had actually ________________ large sums of money in various hiding places in the hovel he called home.

a. benign … decimated
b. ambient … interpolated
c. impecunious … sequestered
d. flaccid … burnished

2. Although many of the pioneers found it difficult at first to cope with the ________________ of frontier life, they were a hardy race who quickly became ________________ such rough-and-tumble living.

a. detritus … decimated by
b. rudiments … importuned by
c. shambles … discomfited by
d. asperities … inured to

3. The "truth-in-advertising" laws that many states have passed were designed to stop crooks and ________________ from making ________________ claims about the products they offer to the unsuspecting public.

a. necromancers … sporadic
b. charlatans … mendacious
c. cabals … eclectic
d. fetishes … laconic

4. The dietician looked ________________ at the sugary cereal and suggested that we ________________ it and try whole-wheat toast and fruit instead.

a. tantamount … cavil
b. obtuse … winnow
c. ambient … attenuate
d. askance … forgo

5. As soon as I heard its ________________ cries for help, I knew that the ________________ animal had once again got its paw caught in the grillwork on the front porch.

a. onerous … defunct
b. obsequious … moribund
c. plaintive … hapless
d. laconic … impeccable

6. In *Of Human Bondage*, W. Somerset Maugham's main character Philip Carey is ________________ by external adversity as well as his own self-consciousness because he was so ________________ as to have been born with a club foot.

a. discomfited … hapless
b. decimated … laconic
c. rebuffed … sporadic
d. requited … benign

7. Though Seneca embraced the tenets of Stoicism in their entirety, Cicero ________________ not just one school of Greek philosophy but, like a true ________________, chose what he thought best from each.

a. espoused … eclectic
b. deprecated … foible
c. discomfited … penitent
d. abrogated … aesthetic

Denotation and Connotation

To speak or write with precision, you need to know both the denotation and the connotation of the words you use. The **denotation** is the literal dictionary meaning of a word. A word's **connotation** is the emotional implications and associations that a word can have. Connotations may be *positive, negative,* or *neutral.*

Consider these synonyms for the word *obsequious*:

amenable　　*complaisant*　　*servile*　　*sycophantic*

Amenable and *complaisant* refer to positive behaviors marked by respect and a disposition to please. *Servile* and *sycophantic* refer to negative behaviors, characterized by fawning and excessive submissiveness.

Look at these examples of words that are similar in denotation but have different connotations.

NEUTRAL	POSITIVE	NEGATIVE
emotional	**sentimental**	**plaintive**
attribute	**virtue**	**foible**
inactive	**relaxed**	**flaccid**

Expressing the Connotation

Read each sentence. Select the word in parentheses that expresses the connotation (positive, negative, or neutral) given at the beginning of the sentence.

positive **1.** The (**ebullient, agitated**) crowd jammed the streets outside the football stadium after the Scouts' surprising victory in overtime.

neutral **2.** The timid student tried to make sense of the (**cavil, observation**) the teacher wrote in the margins of the essay.

neutral **3.** After a difficult loss, the team captain (**deprecated, delineated**) the effort shown by his teammates.

negative **4.** The lifeguards looked (**skeptically, askance**) at the antics of the children who were chasing the birds along the beach.

neutral **5.** Ruth's (**response, rebuff**) to the stranger's offer to take her photograph in front of the White House surprised our entire family.

positive **6.** The desert scene was beautiful, with the sand and palm trees bathed in (**luminous, glaring**) moonlight.

negative **7.** The high winds and torrential rains (**decimated, transformed**) the newly planted rose gardens.

negative **8.** After watching Roger bumble about in the kitchen, I realized he was not a skilled chef, but rather a(n) (**amateur, charlatan**).

Classical Roots

rog—to ask, beg, call

The root *rog* appears in **abrogate** (page 162), meaning "to cancel, to abolish by authoritative action." Some other words based on the same root are listed below.

abrogation	**derogation**	**interrogative**	**supererogatory**
arrogance	**interrogation**	**prorogue**	**surrogate**

From the list of words above, choose the one that corresponds to each of the brief definitions below. Write the word in the blank space in the illustrative sentence below the definition. Use an online or print dictionary if necessary.

1. to discontinue a session of a legislative body; to defer, postpone
The prime minister was determined to ________________ the legislative assembly until all members were present.

2. an act of formal or systematic questioning
The detective asked question after question during the ________________ of the prime suspect.

3. exaggerated self-importance, haughty pride
The king was corrupted by power and, over time, exchanged his humility for ________________.

4. an act or expression that detracts from reputation, value, power, etc. ("*to call down*")
The aid workers deeply resented any ________________ of their motives.

5. a substitute, deputy; a judge in charge of the probate of wills, administration of estates, and appointment of guardians
While my parents were on vacation, my aunt served as a ________________ guardian.

6. a cancellation; the act of repealing or annulling ("*calling off*")
Unfavorable evidence has emerged, forcing the ________________ of the agreement between the two parties.

7. asking a question; having the form or character of a question; a word or sentence that asks a question
In Spanish class, we are learning how to phrase ________________ sentences.

8. performed or observed beyond the degree required; demanded, or expected; unnecessary; superfluous
"We could do with fewer ________________ remarks," the teacher observed.

*Read the following passage, taking note of the **boldface** words and their contexts. These words are among those you will be studying in Unit 13. It may help you to complete the exercises in this Unit if you refer to the way the words are used below.*

More Than Just a Pretty Face

<Profile>

One of many Hollywood stars who **mesmerized** moviegoers of the 1940s was Hedy Lamarr. But it was not only Lamarr's striking looks and dramatic talent that **engendered** admiration in audiences. As fans learned about the actress's life story, many became more interested in Lamarr herself than in the characters she portrayed in her work onscreen.

Born in 1914 in Vienna, Austria, Hedwig Kiesler was the only child of Jewish parents who encouraged their daughter to study ballet and piano. Hedy began her acting career as a teenager, appearing in a number of German films. In 1933, she played a lovesick young wife in a Czech film called *Ecstasy*, a suggestive film derided by **captious** critics as an **affront** to moral decency. Despite the **opprobrium** levied against the film, *Ecstasy* undeniably raised the young actress's profile.

An undated portrait of Hedy Lamarr

Not long after the film's release, Hedy married Fritz Mandl, an arms manufacturer some thirteen years her senior. They were an **incongruous** couple, and Mandl proved a jealous and tyrannical husband. He forbade his wife from pursuing her acting career, and ordered her to accompany him to business meetings. Though frustrated with the relationship, Hedy enjoyed discussions of Mandl's business affairs and became acquainted with weapons systems technology. Soon, dismayed to learn that her husband was a Nazi sympathizer, Hedy fled Austria, escaping both her husband and the Nazis. Various rumors about the **machinations** of her escape would later surface. According to one story, the actress used sleeping pills to drug her maid, who had instructions from Mr. Mandl to see that his wife did not leave the house. Then Hedy put on the maid's uniform and fled through the servants' entrance.

However she escaped, it wasn't long before Hedy arrived in Hollywood and adopted her stage name, Hedy Lamarr. Soon she was starring in motion pictures; she appeared in 18 films during her heyday in the 1940s. Her biggest box-office success was *Samson and Delilah*, the highest-grossing movie of 1949.

While fans at the time recognized Lamarr as an **ethereal** beauty, few were **cognizant** of the celebrity's off-screen pursuits as an inventor. In 1940, in collaboration with her Hollywood neighbor, composer George Antheil, Lamarr developed a "Secret Communication System" designed to make the radio signals used to control missiles harder to detect or jam. With World War II underway, the duo received a patent for the design in 1942. Though their device was never produced, the underlying concept of "frequency hopping" proposed by Lamarr was implemented in a similar form by the United States military in later years, and eventually became an essential feature of wireless communication systems.

In a less **abstruse** contribution to the war effort, Lamarr, with other leading Hollywood actresses, toured major cities to promote the sale of war bonds to help fund the war. Lamarr visited 16 cities in ten days, selling a **putative** $25 million in war bonds in all. Sales received a boost from the unsurprising **efficacy** of Lamarr's offer to kiss any man who purchased $25,000 worth of war bonds—an offer that reportedly raised $7 million in one night.

Lamarr's career declined from 1950, as she gradually fell out of favor with audiences and was no longer considered a bankable **cynosure** in Hollywood. Over time, rumors of less than **decorous** behavior pursued her, including accusations of shoplifting. Lamarr seldom assented to interviews, and after dismissing the rumors as **canards**, she maintained her characteristic silence. Some fans admired Lamarr for not **deigning** to behave in a **contrite** manner, but the rumors proved hard to shake.

Still waters run deep, and there is little doubt that behind the **facade** of silence, Lamarr remained the intelligent and complex person she had always been behind the gloss of Hollywood celebrity. The Electronic Frontier Foundation recognized her talents when it gave Lamarr the Pioneer Award in 1997 for her invention. Lamarr died in 2000.

Audio

For iWords and audio passages, go to **SadlierConnect.com**.

Lamarr gives the V-for-Victory sign while selling war bonds in 1942.

Definitions

Note the spelling, pronunciation, part(s) of speech, and definition(s) of each of the following words. Then write the appropriate form of the word in the blank space in the illustrative sentence(s) following.

1. abstruse (ab strüs′)
(*adj.*) extremely difficult to understand
The physicist tried to explain her ____________ research in the field of quantum mechanics.

2. captious (kap′ shəs)
(*adj.*) excessively ready to find fault; given to petty criticism; intended to trap, confuse, or show up
She is an invariably ____________ critic.

3. contrite (kən trīt′)
(*adj.*) regretful for some misdeed or sin; plagued by a sense of guilt; thoroughly penitent
The convicted felon had the look of someone who was truly ____________ and ready to pay for his crimes.

4. decorous (dek′ ər əs)
(*adj.*) well behaved, dignified, socially proper
On formal occasions, participants are expected to behave in a ____________ manner.

5. efficacy (ef′ ə kə sē)
(*n.*) the power to produce a desired result
The pharmaceutical company has done extensive research to prove the ____________ of the new drug.

6. engender (in jen′ dər)
(*v.*) to bring into existence, give rise to, produce; to come into existence, assume form
The university has made an appealing video in order to ____________ student interest in studying abroad.

7. facade (fə säd′)
(*n.*) the front or face of a building; a surface appearance (as opposed to what may lie behind)
After years of neglect, the sooty ____________ of the structure is finally getting a much needed cleaning.

8. ghoulish (gül′ ish)
(*adj.*) revolting in an unnatural or morbid way; suggestive of someone who robs graves or otherwise preys on the dead
The ____________ practice of grave robbing is motivated by the desire to find and sell valuables.

9. mesmerize (mez′ mə rīz)
(*v.*) to hypnotize, entrance; to fascinate, enthrall, bewitch
The magician was able to ________________ the audience with his fast-moving hands and distracting chatter.

10. opprobrium (ə prō′ brē əm)
(*n.*) disgrace arising from shameful conduct; contempt, reproach
Despite the passage of centuries, ________________ is still attached to the name of the traitor Benedict Arnold.

Using Context

For each item, determine whether the ***boldface*** *word from pages 190–191 makes sense in the context of the sentence. Circle the item numbers next to the six sentences in which the words are used correctly.*

1. If you want to learn about **decorous** behavior, this etiquette and manners blog will probably help you.

2. The musical's upbeat, **contrite** dialogue and witty songs immediately endeared it to the audience as well as critics.

3. Various apps on my phone give me updates on news headlines, sports, the weather, the stock market, and other **opprobrium**.

4. The dispute over the election results threatens to **engender** the small country and, according to some, may even lead to civil war.

5. Books and television shows about vampires, zombies, and other **ghoulish** creatures are extremely popular these days.

6. We hope our plan will be effective, but we will not be able to judge its **efficacy** until we put it into action.

7. After I got to know her, I realized that beneath her **facade** of coolness and confidence, she was a very insecure person.

8. With their rhythmic coming and going, the ocean waves always **mesmerize** me when I am at the beach.

9. The **abstruse** summary of the scientific article was not only unhelpful, but also almost as long as the article itself.

10. He was pleasantly surprised by the **captious** reception his elaborate science project received from the class.

Choosing the Right Word

*Select the **boldface** word that better completes each sentence. You might refer to the passage on pages 188–189 to see how most of these words are used in context. Note that the choices might be related forms of the Unit words.*

1. Workers dismantled and cleaned parts of the Parthenon's exterior (**opprobrium, facade**) during recent restoration work on the temple.

2. Her quiet speech, subdued clothes, and (**decorous, abstruse**) manner made it hard to believe that she was a famous rock star.

3. A government that fails to create reform (**engenders, mesmerizes**) the social unrest that makes violent revolution inevitable.

4. If you had listened to my warnings in the first place, there would be no need for you to feel (**contrite, captious**) now.

5. His unmistakable interest in the gruesome details of the tragedy revealed that he possessed the sensibilities of a (**facade, ghoul**).

6. The audience was so quiet after the curtain fell that I couldn't tell whether they were bored or (**engendered, mesmerized**) by her artistry.

7. "Do we have sufficient evidence at hand," I asked, "to judge the (**efficacy, contrition**) of the new method of teaching reading?"

8. Guests at the formal reception exhibited (**ghoulish, decorous**) behavior.

9. The daring feats of the acrobats on the high wire completely (**engendered, mesmerized**) everyone in the crowd.

10. The (**efficacy, opprobrium**) of history forever attaches itself to the name of Lee Harvey Oswald, the assassin of President Kennedy.

11. The President must always be on his toes because a careless answer to a (**contrite, captious**) question could land him in political hot water.

12. He tried to conceal his lack of scholarship and intellectual depth by using unnecessarily (**efficacious, abstruse**) language.

Completing the Sentence

Choose the word from the word bank that best completes each of the following sentences. Write the correct word or form of the word in the space provided.

abstruse	**contrite**	**efficacy**	**facade**	**mesmerize**
captious	**decorous**	**engender**	**ghoulish**	**opprobrium**

1. Except for a balcony built during the Truman administration, the ____________________ of the White House has remained virtually unchanged since it was constructed.

2. After the battle, camp followers began the ____________________ process of stripping the dead of whatever valuables they possessed.

3. At the risk of appearing a trifle ____________________, I would like to raise a few small objections to the wording of this proposal.

4. Some teachers are able to present the most ____________________ subjects in terms that are clear to all students.

5. The only surefire way to establish the ____________________ of a new drug in treating a disease is to test it "in the field."

6. I didn't really believe that he was sorry for what he had done until I saw the ____________________ expression on his face.

7. There is little evidence that supports the idea that poverty tends to ____________________ poor language skills.

8. The child's conduct during the graduation ceremony may not have been appropriately ____________________, but it wasn't horrendous either.

9. Some historians question whether the disgraced general, Benedict Arnold, really deserves all the ____________________ he has been accorded as America's arch traitor.

10. For more than five minutes she stared at the telegram containing the bad news, as if she were ____________________.

End Set A

Definitions

Note the spelling, pronunciation, part(s) of speech, and definition(s) of each of the following words. Then write the appropriate form of the word in the blank space in the illustrative sentence(s) following.

1. affront
(ə frənt′)
(*n.*) an open or intentional insult; a slight; (*v.*) to insult to one's face; to face in defiance, confront

The student felt that being referred to by number rather than by name was an ____________________ to her dignity.

In the nineteenth century, Irish immigrants to the United States were ____________________ by signs reading: No Irish Need Apply.

2. canard
(kə närd′)
(*n.*) a false rumor, fabricated story

The tabloid journalist was responsible for spreading the ____________________ about the candidate's mental health.

3. cognizant
(käg′ ni zənt)
(*adj.*) aware, knowledgeable, informed; having jurisdiction

Police officers must make sure that crime suspects are made ____________________ of their rights before they are questioned.

4. cynosure
(sī′ nə shür)
(*n.*) the center of attraction, attention, or interest; something that serves to guide or direct

For over a century, the Statue of Liberty has been the ____________________ for millions of immigrants entering New York Harbor.

5. deign
(dān)
(*v.*) to think it appropriate or suitable to one's dignity to do something; to condescend

The enlisted men were surprised that the four-star general ____________________ to speak to them in the camp.

6. desiccated
(des′ ə kā tid)
(*adj., part.*) thoroughly dried out; divested of spirit or vitality; arid and uninteresting

The cornfield was ____________________ by the scorching sun after the long, hot summer without rain.

7. ethereal
(i thēr′ ē əl)
(*adj.*) light, airy, delicate; highly refined; suggesting what is heavenly (rather than earthbound)

The Renaissance painter Fra Angelico captured the ____________________ beauty of angels in his frescoes.

8. incongruous
(in kän′ grü əs)
(*adj.*) not in keeping, unsuitable, incompatible

Abraham Lincoln, the backwoods lawyer, and Mary Todd, the socialite, seemed an ____________________ couple.

9. machination (mak ə nā′ shən) (*n.*) a crafty, scheming, or underhanded action designed to accomplish some (usually evil) end

Shakespeare's Othello was the victim not only of Iago's evil ____________ but also of his own jealous nature.

10. putative (pyü′ tə tiv) (*adj.*) generally regarded as such; reputed; hypothesized, inferred

Ancient Celtic rituals and ceremonies are the ____________ origins of some of our modern Halloween customs.

Using Context

For each item, determine whether the ***boldface*** *word from pages 194–195 makes sense in the context of the sentence. Circle the item numbers next to the six sentences in which the words are used correctly.*

1. "Do you think you'll **deign** to speak with me once you're a famous actress?" I asked my best friend after her impressive performance in the play.
2. The tornado tore through the town leaving behind an **ethereal** scene of destruction.
3. The principal instruments used in songs from the "synthpop" genre include electronic keyboards, synthesizers, and other forms of musical **machination**.
4. **Cognizant** of his surroundings, he absentmindedly walked into a construction site.
5. The **putative** author of the unsigned letter arguing against school uniforms is a friend who values her unique sense of style.
6. I know your sense of humor involves poking fun at everyone, but people who don't know you well may view your teasing as a personal **affront**.
7. I like to think I can maintain my **cynosure** in any situation, but this unexpected exam really rattles me.
8. Your lectures about the importance of keeping a clean house are completely **incongruous** with your consistently messy home.
9. The **desiccated** blackberry brambles you see along the coastline dried out after the harsh saltwater waves rushed through them during the storm surge.
10. When your story was proven to be a **canard**, you lost all credibility with those who once trusted you.

Choosing the Right Word

*Select the **boldface** word that better completes each sentence. You might refer to the passage on pages 188–189 to see how most of these words are used in context. Note that the choices might be related forms of the Unit words.*

1. The 1938 radio broadcast by Orson Welles that described a Martian invasion is on many lists of the greatest (**canards, machinations**) of the twentieth century.

2. I resent your nasty question about whether or not I will "(**deign, affront**) to speak to ordinary students" after I'm elected class president.

3. The play is so peopled with spirits and other incorporeal beings that it has the (**ethereal, putative**) quality of a dream.

4. The candidate's "shocking revelation" about his opponent was later shown to be nothing more than a malicious (**canard, cynosure**).

5. Sitting in the back of the cathedral, I strained to hear the lovely, (**ethereal, desiccated**) voices of the children wafting down from the choir loft.

6. In my youthful folly, I inadvertently (**affronted, deigned**) the very people whose aid I was attempting to enlist.

7. For any actor, it is a unique thrill to know that when you are alone on stage, you are the (**canard, cynosure**) of hundreds of pairs of eyes.

8. Like many people who are completely wrapped up in themselves, she simply isn't (**cognizant, incongruous**) of the larger world around her.

9. Philologists believe that many Western languages can be traced back to a (**putative, ethereal**) parent tongue known as Indo-European.

10. The book describes in great detail the odious (**machinations, affronts**) involved in Hitler's rise to power in Germany.

11. He acts like someone whose vital juices have long since dried up, leaving only a drab and (**desiccated, cognizant**) shell behind.

12. It has been said that humor is essentially the yoking of (**incongruous, ethereal**) elements within a familiar or recognizable framework.

Completing the Sentence

Choose the word from the word bank that best completes each of the following sentences. Write the correct word or form of the word in the space provided.

affront	**cognizant**	**deign**	**ethereal**	**machination**
canard	**cynosure**	**desiccated**	**incongruous**	**putative**

1. The pages of the old book were so ____________________ that they began to crumble as soon as we touched them.

2. No one knows for sure who really wrote the scene, but Shakespeare is generally regarded as its ____________________ author.

3. Am I supposed to feel honored simply because that arrogant lout sometimes ____________________ to nod vaguely in my direction?

4. The longer I study this country's history, the more ____________________ I become of my rich heritage of freedom.

5. Only a thoroughly naive and gullible person would actually believe every preposterous ____________________ that circulates in this school.

6. The cherubic faces and ____________________ voices of the choristers almost moved me to tears.

7. The ____________________ of the unscrupulous wheeler-dealers involved in that unsavory scandal boggle the imagination.

8. What could be more ____________________ than the 6-foot, 7-inch center on the basketball team dolled up in baby clothes for the class play!

9. To be the ____________________ of all eyes could be the joyous fulfillment of a dream or the unhappy realization of a nightmare.

10. His fantastic stories about his academic, athletic, financial, and romantic achievements are a(n) ____________________ to common sense.

End Set B

Synonyms

Choose the word or form of the word from this Unit that is the same or most nearly the same in meaning as the ***boldface*** *word or expression in the phrase. Write that word on the line. Use a dictionary if necessary.*

1. brought **shame** on the whole family ______________
2. the **focal point** of the city ______________
3. the **exterior** of the cathedral ______________
4. a **fabrication** not supported by facts ______________
5. **stooped** to give a few interviews ______________
6. **hypnotized** by his deep voice ______________
7. a **fiendish** interest in death ______________
8. disliked for his **nit-picking** tendencies ______________
9. the **effectiveness** of the stop sign ______________
10. foiled the **schemes** of the villain ______________
11. the **parched** desert landscape ______________
12. **begets** mistrust by covering up mistakes ______________
13. **esoteric** concepts developed by experts ______________
14. **conscious** of our mutual responsibilities ______________
15. the **jarring** reunion of longtime rivals ______________

Antonyms

Choose the word or form of the word from this Unit that is most nearly opposite in meaning to the ***boldface*** *word or expression in the phrase. Write that word on the line. Use a dictionary if necessary.*

1. the **known** whereabouts of the fugitive ______________
2. the **unrepentant** ringleaders of the riot ______________
3. a network of **thick** spider webs ______________
4. took it as a personal **compliment** ______________
5. the **unseemly** appearance of the judge ______________

Writing: Words in Action

Suppose a publishing company has hired you to promote an upcoming biography of Hedy Lamarr. Write a press release to interest people in Lamarr's life and persuade them to buy the book. Use at least two details from the passage (pages 188–189) and three or more words from this Unit.

Vocabulary in Context

Some of the words you have studied in this Unit appear in ***boldface*** *type. Read the passage below, and then circle the letter of the correct answer for each word as it is used in context.*

For several decades now, intellectual property has been one of the most dynamic sectors of legal practice. Far from becoming **desiccated** relics gathering dust in law libraries, tomes on copyright, patents, and trademark law appear ever more frequently, especially since the Internet has raised the stakes for high-profile creative industries such as music and book publishing.

One of the most dramatically contested areas of intellectual property is patent law. Patents confer on inventors a **putative** right or title for a set period to make use of and profit from their invention, as well as to exclude others from making, using, or selling it. The first recorded patent was granted in 1421 in the Italian city of Florence to an engineer named Filippo Brunelleschi, giving him a three-year monopoly on the manufacture of a barge with hoisting gear designed to transport marble. In the United States, the framers of the Constitution specifically included copyrights and patents in Article I, Section 8, which gives Congress the power to "promote science and the useful arts, by securing for limited times . . . the exclusive right to their respective writings and discoveries." The original term for patents was fourteen years, which has now been extended to twenty.

Patent law now imposes three requirements on inventions to promote the law's **efficacy**: inventions must be truly novel, nonobvious, and useful. Contention over these requirements has ranged from the comic to the **ghoulish**, however. Developing countries are especially upset about industrial nations' avidity to patent natural plants and processes—for example, turmeric and neem in India, which have been used medicinally for thousands of years. Such nations condemn this **affront** as biopiracy. These protestors may seem **captious**, but pharmaceutical disputes can involve millions of dollars.

---

1. **Desiccated** relics are
- **a.** uninteresting
- **b.** thriving
- **c.** depreciated
- **d.** ungainly

2. A **putative** right is
- **a.** verified
- **b.** mercurial
- **c.** esoteric
- **d.** reputed

3. The **efficacy** of a law largely consists in its
- **a.** promotion
- **b.** publication
- **c.** simplicity
- **d.** potency

4. The word **ghoulish** most nearly means
- **a.** collaborative
- **b.** hilarious
- **c.** monstrous
- **d.** sober

5. An **affront** is a(n)
- **a.** insult
- **b.** eulogy
- **c.** lamentation
- **d.** litany

6. You are **captious** if you are
- **a.** victorious
- **b.** faultfinding
- **c.** resplendent
- **d.** predatory

*Read the following passage, taking note of the **boldface** words and their contexts. These words are among those you will be studying in Unit 14. It may help you to complete the exercises in this Unit if you refer to the way the words are used below.*

Artificial Intelligence and Social Robots

<Technical Essay>

Robots are machines programmed to interact with their surroundings. They can be stationary or mobile. They can be stand-alone systems or "insects" in a fleet. Some robots perform household chores or provide entertainment, but the most common are industrial robots **consigned** to assembly lines and service robots used for repetitive tasks such as milking cows. Some critics complain that the use of industrial and service robots can foster unemployment. Proponents claim the use of robots frees human workers from tedious physical labor that many are **loath** to do, enabling people to do more satisfying work.

The term "robot" appeared for the first time in a 1920 fantasy play by Karel Capek, and comes from a Czech word meaning "forced labor." In Capek's **visionary** tale, robots develop self-awareness, tire of servitude, and stage a **coup** that destroys the human race. Of course, most scientists would be skeptical and **gainsay** claims about the **imminent** threat of robots rebelling against humanity. However, the notion that robots might learn to think for themselves can no longer be treated as an impossibility.

Robotics developed with **febrile** intensity in the 1990s, following advances in the field of artificial intelligence. The breakthroughs improved computer systems' capacity to perform tasks involving perception, speech recognition, decision-making, translation, and related skills. Early attempts to design intelligent robots focused on simple interactions with the environment, like getting a machine to learn to navigate down a hallway. With time, scientists began to produce robots that perceive subtle features of the world around them, even distinguishing **cacophonous** laughter from harmonious singing. Recent efforts have focused on robots that cooperate with humans by using realistic social behaviors. These "social robots" engage in interactive behaviors and respond to human actions. Some even interpret emotions normally **manifest** only to humans and make appropriate responses, including facial expressions.

In order to make interaction with social robots feel natural, many are designed to look like humans, animals, or cartoon-like

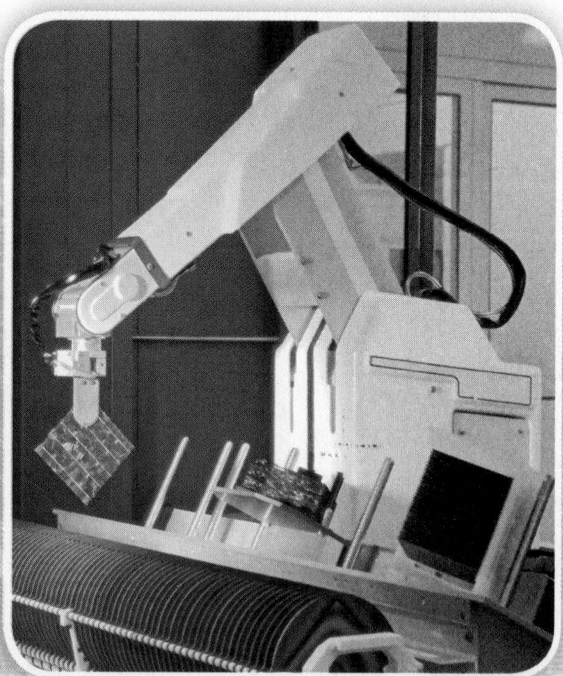

A robot completes repetitive tasks at a solar cell manufacturer.

The robot Alex Hubo was made to look like Albert Einstein.

characters. One Korean-made robot, modeled after famed scientist Albert Einstein, has a rubber face shaped to resemble the **wizened** old physicist in his later years. Designers took great pains to make the face lifelike, down to **minutiae** like a bushy mustache, fuzzy eyebrows, and gleaming eyes. Beneath its familiar appearance, the robot contains sophisticated artificial intelligence software, 32 motors to guide facial movements, and two cameras housed in its eyes. The Einstein robot has learned to mimic a range of facial expressions, from a **beatific** smile to a wide-eyed look of surprise.

Researchers are exploring a variety of potential uses for social robots. People whose **innate** ability to interpret emotions is impaired might benefit from interaction with social robots. Emotionally responsive robots could provide companionship for the elderly and help them operate digital devices. Law-enforcement robots could help police by detecting concealed weapons and bombs. They could even take measurements of heart rate, respiration, and body temperature to recognize the **chicanery** of a lying suspect.

Some researchers and entrepreneurs claim that social robots will soon provide a **nostrum** for a range of socioeconomic ills. It is more likely that decades of research will be required before social robots have a deep impact on human life and work. However long it takes, it is clear that the die is cast. Intelligent social robots are destined to become increasingly integrated into human society.

Georgia Tech University developed this social robot named Simon.

Audio

For iWords and audio passages, go to **SadlierConnect.com**.

Definitions

Note the spelling, pronunciation, part(s) of speech, and definition(s) of each of the following words. Then write the appropriate form of the word in the blank space in the illustrative sentence(s) following.

1. beatific
(bē ə tif′ ik)
(*adj.*) blissful; rendering or making blessed
During the awards ceremony, the gold medal winner had a positively ____________________ expression on her face.

2. blandishment
(blan′ dish mənt)
(*n.*, often *pl.*) anything designed to flatter or coax; sweet talk, apple-polishing
The king was often influenced by subtle ____________________.

3. chicanery
(shi kā′ nə rē)
(*n.*) trickery, deceptive practices or tactics, double-dealing
The accountants used legal ____________________ to cover up the company's shaky financial position.

4. coup
(kü)
(*n.*) a highly successful stroke, masterstroke, tour de force, act, plan, or stratagem; a sudden takeover of power or leadership
The surprise ____________________ by high-ranking military officers toppled the weak government in a matter of hours.

5. febrile
(feb′ rīl)
(*adj.*) feverish; pertaining to or marked by fever; frenetic
The journalist wrote with ____________________ intensity.

6. innate
(i nāt′)
(*adj.*) natural, inborn, inherent; built-in
Musical excellence often comes from ____________________ ability.

7. minutiae
(mə nü′ shē ə)
(*pl. n.*) small or trivial details, trifling matters
Because the researcher was too concerned with ____________________, she was unlikely to make an original discovery.

8. nostrum
(näs′ trəm)
(*n.*) an alleged cure-all; a remedy or scheme of questionable effectiveness
The federal Food and Drug Administration was created in part to keep unsavory characters from peddling ____________________ to the public.

9. pariah (par ī' ə) — (*n.*) one who is rejected by a social group or organization

In most of the world today, those who are suffering from the disease of leprosy are no longer treated as ____________________.

10. wizened (wiz' ənd) — (*adj., part.*) dry, shrunken, and wrinkled (often as the result of aging)

The ____________________ old woman walked with the aid of a cane.

Using Context

*For each item, determine whether the **boldface** word from pages 202–203 makes sense in the context of the sentence. Circle the item numbers next to the six sentences in which the words are used correctly.*

1. The movie studio executives agreed that acquiring the movie rights to the popular series of novels was a real **coup**.
2. Despite her **wizened** appearance, the elderly shopkeeper was surprisingly bubbly and energetic.
3. The **beatific** vision of the happy children frolicking on the sunlit beach delighted their parents.
4. A little plastic model of a bride and groom is a common **blandishment** for a wedding cake.
5. We always look forward to the food, fun, thrills, and **chicanery** of the annual summer carnival.
6. Why are we arguing over **minutiae** when there are so many other important issues that we need to discuss?
7. The keynote speaker rose from her seat alongside the stage, stood behind the **nostrum**, and began her address in a clear, steady voice.
8. People journeyed from near and far to consult the esteemed **pariah** for his advice on social concerns.
9. He launched into his new exercise program with **febrile** energy, but whether he will be able to sustain the effort is yet to be determined.
10. Geese and other migrating animals have an **innate** sense of direction.

Choosing the Right Word

*Select the **boldface** word that better completes each sentence. You might refer to the passage on pages 200–201 to see how most of these words are used in context. Note that the choices might be related forms of the Unit words.*

1. After he killed Alexander Hamilton in a duel, Aaron Burr found himself no longer a respected statesman, but a social and political (**coup, pariah**).

2. The kind of financial (**minutiae, chicanery**) involved in bringing off that deal may not have been illegal, but it was certainly unethical.
3. After it had been left to rot in the sun for a few days, the plump little apple began to take on the (**beatific, wizened**) appearance of a prune.
4. Although I play a fair game of chess, I'm not capable of the brilliant (**coups, chicanery**) that mark a true master of the game.
5. Only when we tried to implement the plan did its (**innate, febrile**) defects become clear to us.
6. Someone who "can't see the forest for the trees" is usually too concerned with (**minutiae, nostrums**) to be aware of the overall picture.
7. When he took his first bite of Mother's famous coconut custard pie, a look of (**innate, beatific**) joy spread over his face.
8. In September 1973, President Salvador Allende of Chile was ousted in a (**coup, blandishment**) organized by the military.
9. The (**wizened, febrile**) tempo of the symphony's opening movement gives way to a placid and stately largo in the next.
10. It is a rare leader indeed who can tell the public unpleasant truths without evasions or (**pariahs, blandishments**).
11. After touching the baby's (**febrile, imminent**) cheek, Harry called the doctor.
12. The solution to our problems is to be found in long-term programs of social planning, not in easy (**pariahs, nostrums**).

Completing the Sentence

Choose the word from the word bank that best completes each of the following sentences. Write the correct word or form of the word in the space provided.

beatific	**chicanery**	**febrile**	**minutiae**	**pariah**
blandishment	**coup**	**innate**	**nostrum**	**wizened**

1. Though the ability to paint is probably a(n) ________________ gift, it can certainly be improved by training and practice.

2. When it became clear just how shamelessly he had treated his brother, he became a virtual ________________ in his own family.

3. If you spend all your time on ________________, you won't have any left for really important matters.

4. Suddenly I was overcome by such a feeling of ________________ peace that I began to wonder whether I was still on earth.

5. Though her body had become bent and ________________ with age, her mind was as alert and active as ever.

6. The nation's economic ills call for a variety of remedies; they cannot be cured by any single, miraculous ________________.

7. Some Civil War generals weren't professional soldiers and got their jobs through pulling strings and other forms of political ________________.

8. Since I was brought up in a sleepy country town, I found it very hard to adjust to the ________________ pace of big-city life.

9. Just when it seemed that defeat was inevitable, she pulled off a dazzling ________________ that totally discomfited her opponent.

10. Only a fool would have succumbed to the cloying ________________ of that smooth-talking rascal!

End Set A

Definitions

Note the spelling, pronunciation, part(s) of speech, and definition(s) of each of the following words. Then write the appropriate form of the word in the blank space in the illustrative sentence(s) following.

1. behemoth
(bi hē′ məth)
(*n.*) a creature of enormous size, power, or appearance
The Loch Ness monster is a famous ________________.

2. cacophonous
(kə käf′ ə nəs)
(*adj.*) harsh-sounding, raucous, discordant, dissonant
The scene opened with ________________ laughter coming from witches gathered around a steaming cauldron.

3. consign
(kən sīn′)
(*v.*) to give over to another's care, charge, or control; to entrust, deliver; to set apart for a special use
The ship's captain ________________ many duties to her trusted first mate.

4. euphemism
(yü′ fə miz əm)
(*n.*) a mild or inoffensive expression used in place of a harsh or unpleasant one; a substitute
Common ________________ for *die* include the expressions *pass away* and *go to the other side*.

5. gainsay
(gān′ sā)
(*v.*) to deny, contradict, controvert; to dispute, oppose
Some wished to ________________ the conclusions of the United States Supreme Court in the matter of the 2000 presidential election.

6. imminent
(im′ ə nənt)
(*adj.*) about to happen, threatening
An ________________ hurricane forced the islanders back to the mainland.

7. loath
(lōth)
(*adj.*) unwilling, reluctant, disinclined
My hardworking grandfather was ________________ to retire.

8. manifest
(man′ ə fest)
(*adj.*) clear, evident to the eyes or mind; (*v.*) to show plainly, exhibit, evince; (*n.*) a list of cargo and/or passengers
It was ________________ to many nineteenth-century Americans that the nation was destined to extend to the Pacific Ocean.
When the man began to ________________ signs of hearing loss, he went to a specialist.
The passenger ________________ helps investigators find out who is on board a plane.

9. moratorium (môr ə tōr′ ē əm) — (*n.*) a suspension of activity; an official waiting period; an authorized period of delay

The conference was held to try to negotiate a ________________ on arms sales to both sides of the conflict.

10. visionary (vizh′ ə ner ē) — (*adj.*) not practical, lacking in realism; having the nature of a fantasy or dream; (*n.*) one given to far-fetched ideas; a dreamer or seer characterized by vision or foresight

Ideas that once were considered ________________ often become widely accepted over time.

The Reverend Martin Luther King, Jr., was a ________________ whose dreams inspired the American civil rights movement.

Using Context

*For each item, determine whether the **boldface** word from pages 206–207 makes sense in the context of the sentence. Circle the item numbers next to the six sentences in which the words are used correctly.*

1. A few minutes after getting the infant to sleep, I heard the roar of thunder and knew that the sound of a crying baby was **imminent**.
2. The love between the soon-to-be married couple was **manifest** on both of their faces as they joyfully recited their vows.
3. The dog must have appeared to be a **behemoth** to the chipmunk, which ran off in fear.
4. **Loath** to see my cousin after he had been abroad for the past year, I ran over to hug him.
5. She tried to **consign** her tears after losing the swim race, but she cried on the bench.
6. It's ideal to have a balance of imaginative thinkers whose ideas are **visionary** and practical thinkers who focus on day-to-day matters.
7. I went to the library to work, but the low **moratorium** of people talking was a distraction.
8. We attempted to **gainsay** the local community hall for a rehearsal space, but to no avail.
9. Even though my teacher did not directly say my short stories were bad, her repeated use of the **euphemism** "needs work" was enough to dash my hopes of becoming an author.
10. The **cacophonous** sound of clashing instruments and off-key voices does not appeal to me.

Choosing the Right Word

*Select the **boldface** word that better completes each sentence. You might refer to the passage on pages 200–201 to see how most of these words are used in context. Note that the choices might be related forms of the Unit words.*

1. Many scientists view Nicolaus Copernicus as a (**visionary, euphemism**), not simply a talented mathematician and the founder of modern astronomy.

2. I discovered my grandmother's name on the (**moratorium, manifest**) of a ship that carried immigrants from Italy to Boston in 1919.

3. The plan is certainly ingenious, but it strikes me as far too (**visionary, imminent**) to serve as the basis for practical legislation.

4. It didn't make me any happier to learn that my firing was being referred to (**euphemistically, cacophonously**) as a "termination."

5. No one who knows the facts would venture to (**gainsay, consign**) your claim to have done your utmost to improve this community.

6. Although I am (**imminent, loath**) to boast, I must acknowledge my superior qualities as a student, athlete, financier, and all-round social luminary.

7. Accidents at nuclear power plants have prompted some people to agitate for a (**moratorium, behemoth**) on the construction of such facilities.

8. "Does anybody dare to (**manifest, gainsay**) my decision to paint the house orange?" Uncle Max inquired with a twinkle in his eye.

9. The (**cacophony, moratorium**) that suddenly greeted my ears made me suspect that a fox had somehow gotten into the henhouse.

10. "As soon as we received the order," I said, "we crated the equipment and (**gainsaid, consigned**) it to the buyer in Atlanta."

11. "How much of a chance do you suppose a 98-pound weakling like me actually stands against that 320-pound (**visionary, behemoth**)?" I asked incredulously.

12. (**Imminent, Loath**) disaster stared us in the face when we were thrown for a loss and then fumbled the ball on our own five-yard line.

Completing the Sentence

Choose the word from the word bank that best completes each of the following sentences. Write the correct word or form of the word in the space provided.

behemoth	**consign**	**gainsay**	**loath**	**moratorium**
cacophonous	**euphemism**	**imminent**	**manifest**	**visionary**

1. Some people enjoy the type of atonal music written by such composers as Arnold Schoenberg; others find it ____________________.

2. No matter what ____________________ you use to describe his conduct, you can't disguise the fact he betrayed his best friend.

3. However much I may dispute your views, I will never ____________________ your right to hold them.

4. Before you dismiss her as just another impractical ____________________, think of how many great inventors were once regarded as mere "cranks."

5. We were all surprised that someone with the reputation of a frivolous playboy could ____________________ such courage and determination.

6. One way to bring relief to small farmers who cannot meet their mortgage payments is to declare a temporary ____________________ on foreclosures.

7. On the first play, our diminutive quarterback was "sacked" by a veritable ____________________ of a linebacker, ominously nicknamed "Bone Crusher."

8. When the swollen river threatened to overflow its banks, a devastating flood seemed ____________________.

9. You may be, as you say, "____________________ to leave such a fascinating book," but I'm telling you right now to take out the garbage!

10. In a touching ceremony, the soldiers ____________________ the body of their fallen leader to the grave and her memory to their hearts.

End Set B

Synonyms

*Choose the word or form of the word from this Unit that is the same or most nearly the same in meaning as the **boldface** word or expression in the phrase. Write that word on the line. Use a dictionary if necessary.*

1. the salesman's miracle **elixir** ______________
2. the **disharmonious** student band ______________
3. a **replacement** for the word *ugly* ______________
4. **transferred** to an underground facility ______________
5. an **intrinsic** capacity for learning ______________
6. **transcendent** vision of another world ______________
7. achieved a major **feat** ______________
8. fascinated by the **trivia** of celebrity gossip ______________
9. when **mammoths** roamed Earth ______________
10. feeble and **shriveled** appearance ______________
11. considered an **outcast** by her neighbors ______________
12. checked the **list** for survivors ______________
13. open to the **enticements** of lobbyists ______________
14. prepared for the **delay** ______________
15. warned of an **impending** investigation ______________

Antonyms

*Choose the word or form of the word from this Unit that is most nearly opposite in meaning to the **boldface** word or expression in the phrase. Write that word on the line. Use a dictionary if necessary.*

1. was **willing** to make a compromise ______________
2. **frigid** temperatures ______________
3. a **realistic** blueprint for change ______________
4. **confirm** the politician's contributions ______________
5. the lawyer's **fair practices** ______________

Writing: Words in Action

Imagine you work for a company that designs and manufactures social robots. Write an editorial that explains the ways in which their use will improve the lives of many people. Use details from the passage (pages 200–201), personal experiences, and three or more words from this Unit to support your points.

Vocabulary in Context

Some of the words you have studied in this Unit appear in ***boldface*** *type. Read the passage below, and then circle the letter of the correct answer for each word as it is used in context.*

As time goes by, robots become an ever more common sight. They have long been essential equipment in factories, for example, and their exploits in space, as well as undersea, are often reported. Despite the economic challenge they pose to some workers' jobs, there has been no **moratorium** on their development.

Perhaps the most recent arena for high-tech robot activity is the hospital operating room. Over a decade's worth of experience has shown that the purported advantage of robotic surgery is not a mere **blandishment**. Analysis of such procedures has demonstrated that they are more rapid and precise, as well as considerably less invasive, resulting in more favorable outcomes, briefer hospital stays, and faster patient recovery.

It is a common misconception that the robot actually controls the surgery. In one program approved by the Food and Drug Administration (FDA) in 2000, a surgeon with the aid of a two-part mechanical **behemoth** coordinates procedures: a master console unit and a four-armed patient's side cart. This system always requires a human operator, so the surgeon has scarcely been sidelined or become a **pariah** around the hospital.

So far, at least, after two million or so robo-surgery operations, it is hard to **gainsay** the positive aspects. Far from being a **euphemism** for patient neglect, robo-surgery may soon become the patient's new gold standard in health care. The $2 million price tag on console-side cart units may well come down, and the already formidable precision of the robots may yet improve. Surgeons themselves seem supportive, not least because robots are likely to relieve occupational hazards such as neck strain and pressures on the shoulders and back. "The physical demands of surgery aren't talked about much," remarks one British surgeon. "However, operating sitting down using a robot means I could keep going for longer than I had thought."

---

1. A **moratorium** is a(n)
a. postponement **c.** escalation
b. opinion poll **d.** imprimatur

2. The word **blandishment** most nearly means
a. cajolery **c.** procrastination
b. predilections **d.** uniformity

3. A robot might be called a **behemoth** if it is
a. automated **c.** hard to operate
b. not efficient **d.** very large

4. A **pariah** is a(n)
a. eminence **c.** outcast
b. hostage **d.** recluse

5. To **gainsay** is to
a. corroborate **c.** relegate
b. deny **d.** parlay

6. The word **euphemism** most nearly means
a. substitute **c.** allusion
b. encomium **d.** salutation

*Read the following passage, taking note of the **boldface** words and their contexts. These words are among those you will be studying in Unit 15. It may help you to complete the exercises in this Unit if you refer to the way the words are used below.*

Private Life in the Public Eye

<Humorous Essay>

There are many reasons to keep a private diary. Jotting down your thoughts helps you sort out **nascent** feelings. Sketching plans helps you make way toward your goals. Whatever your reasons, keeping a diary is a perfect way to exercise your **inviolable** right to take yourself too seriously. The only problem is, it's hard to keep your private scribblings safe from prying eyes. To keep a diary is to run the risk that your secret thoughts might be discovered by some snooping relative or friend, even **promulgated** round the world, like the evening news or the latest scandal on the Internet.

One of history's great examples of private thoughts gone public is a diary penned in the seventeenth century by Samuel Pepys (1633–1703). Pepys was an ambitious man who climbed the ranks of English society by skillful work and diligent networking, eventually becoming a member of Parliament, a Fellow of the Royal Society, and Secretary for the Admiralty. On account of his public achievements, we should consider him a leading man of his day. But the diary he left to his **progeny**, having slipped into the records of history, provides another **aperture** through which to view the man.

Visscher's view of London, 1616

In the pages of his private thoughts, Pepys, for all his hard work, high culture, and dignified connections, seems a man of **restive** habits and **mutable** character. He wrestles with his vices in his diary, time and again falling short of moral **rectitude** and raking over the ashes of his chief **iniquities**: his **epicurean** love of wine, his addiction to the theater, and his lust for women other than his wife.

To the historian, Pepys's diary provides an insider's glimpse of the English Restoration: meetings with the king and other men of high office, eyewitness accounts of the Great Fire and the Great Plague of London, and views on the politics of war and peace. But the casual reader—who might not care a **pittance** for international affairs of the seventeenth century—is more apt to enjoy the diary's personal anecdotes. Mr. Pepys rolls over one night in his sleep accidentally to smash his wife in the nose with his elbow. Another evening, he's threatening to fling her poor dog out the window. For months on end he's racked with jealousy, afraid his wife might have an eye for other men, though he doesn't let the sentiment interfere with his own thoughts on comely women. He criticizes the king's skill at tennis, reports on the monarch's drinking habits and mistresses, and complains about the flatterers who praise their ruler far more than he deserves.

For all the notable accomplishments of his public life, Samuel Pepys is most commonly remembered as a funny fellow who kept a diary and who could not **subsist** without wine, plays, or the other **amenities** of his times. His honesty and enthusiasm for the details of his life might be worth a **panegyric**, but for some of his flaws the man deserves to be **pilloried**. We would know nothing of his shortcomings if it weren't for the **improvident** decision, or perhaps the odd pride, that led Pepys to leave his diary behind. On the other hand, if it weren't for that diary, most of us would not know the man at all. This very public legacy is a reminder to anyone who aspires to be a "private" diarist. Be careful what you commit to print!

King Charles II was the subject of many of Pepys's diary entries.

Audio

For iWords and audio passages, go to **SadlierConnect.com**.

Definitions

Note the spelling, pronunciation, part(s) of speech, and definition(s) of each of the following words. Then write the appropriate form of the word in the blank space in the illustrative sentence(s) following.

1. **aperture** (ap′ ər chər)
(*n.*) an opening, gap, hole; orifice
After the earthquake, rain and cold came through the ______________ in the wall of the damaged house.

2. **dissidence** (dis′ ə dəns)
(*n.*) a difference of opinion; discontent
When the commanding officer announced that all leave was cancelled, there was widespread ______________ in the ranks.

3. **improvident** (im präv′ ə dənt)
(*adj.*) not thrifty; failing to plan ahead
Some people are so ______________ that despite high incomes they struggle to make ends meet.

4. **nascent** (nā′ sənt)
(*adj.*) just beginning to exist or develop; having just come into existence
Recent public opinion polls registered ______________ opposition to the proposed tax increase.

5. **obeisance** (ō bē′ səns)
(*n.*) a deep bow or other body movement indicating respect or submission; deference, homage
Upon entering the throne room, each courtier made a respectful ______________ before the king and queen.

6. **pillory** (pil′ ə rē)
(*n.*) a device for publicly punishing offenders; a means for exposing one to public contempt or ridicule; (*v.*) to expose to public contempt or ridicule
The ______________ was placed in the center of town so that everyone could view the outlaws and their shame.
The candidate tried to ______________ her political opponent by suggesting that he had ties to organized crime.

7. **pittance** (pit′ əns)
(*n.*) a woefully meager allowance, wage, or portion
In comparison to the overwhelming need for food and medicine, the shipment was a mere ______________.

8. **progeny** (präj′ ə nē)
(*n.*) descendants, offspring, children, followers, disciples
The Bill of Rights guarantees certain civil rights and protections to us and our ______________.

9. restive (res′ tiv)
(*adj.*) restless, hard to manage, balky
The ______________________ horse had not been taken out of the stable for five days.

10. subsist (səb sist′)
(*v.*) to have existence; to remain alive, manage to make a living or maintain life; to persist or continue
Peasants in nineteenth-century Ireland were able to ______________________ almost exclusively on potatoes.

Using Context

*For each item, determine whether the **boldface** word from pages 214–215 makes sense in the context of the sentence. Circle the item numbers next to the six sentences in which the words are used correctly.*

1. The manager preferred not to **pillory** the employee in front of her coworkers for her lateness; instead he reprimanded her privately.

2. It may be **improvident**, but it is not impossible for lightning to strike the same place twice.

3. During a violent volcanic eruption, lava or ash shoots up through an **aperture** in Earth's crust.

4. The growing **dissidence** in the American colonies gradually led to a full-blown revolution.

5. Advisors from several countries will help develop a plan for holding elections in the **nascent** democracy.

6. Although his inheritance was an enormous **pittance**, he managed to spend all of the money within a year.

7. The **restive** lullaby had the desired effect, and the children were asleep even before it ended.

8. The explorers followed the river all the way to its **progeny** in a mountain lake.

9. The rebels refused to submit with **obeisance** to the cruel regime and vowed to fight for their freedom instead.

10. It surprises me that an animal as large and powerful as an elephant is able to **subsist** on grass and other vegetation.

Choosing the Right Word

*Select the **boldface** word that better completes each sentence. You might refer to the passage on pages 212–213 to see how most of these words are used in context. Note that the choices might be related forms of the Unit words.*

1. Petty criminals in medieval England were often placed in stocks or (**progeny, pillories**) and subjected to public humiliation.

2. The cost of living has risen so sharply that a salary that was adequate a decade ago is now no more than a mere (**aperture, pittance**).

3. Liberty (**subsists, pillories**) only as long as people have the intelligence to know their rights and the courage to defend them.

4. One cannot expect a (**restive, nascent**) democracy to go through its early years without experiencing serious growing pains.

5. Writers often regard their works as their (**dissidence, progeny**) in much the same way as other people regard their pets as family members.

6. Like so many others of his generation, he paid unquestioning (**pittance, obeisance**) to the accepted symbols of material success.

7. The novel centers on a(n) (**improvident, nascent**) young man who squanders his inheritance and dies in the poorhouse.

8. The visitors lowered their voices and made (**obeisance, pillory**) to the distinguished gentleman who was beckoning them toward the castle entrance.

9. As the speaker's remarks became more inflammatory, the crowd grew more sullen and (**improvident, restive**).

10. There was a loophole in the law, and through this (**aperture, obeisance**) the defendant escaped the legal consequences of his crime.

11. I realize the official made a serious mistake, but that is no reason to (**pillory, subsist**) him so unmercifully in the press.

12. Religious (**obeisance, dissidence**) was one of the motives that led many people to found colonies in North America.

Completing the Sentence

Choose the word from the word bank that best completes each of the following sentences. Write the correct word or form of the word in the space provided.

aperture	**improvident**	**obeisance**	**pittance**	**restive**
dissidence	**nascent**	**pillory**	**progeny**	**subsist**

1. Though I'm by no means ________________ with my money, I don't hoard it either.

2. The liberties that we have inherited from our forefathers are a sacred trust that we must pass on undiminished to our ________________.

3. The ________________ on most cameras can be adjusted to admit more or less light, as required.

4. The Bible tells us that visitors to the court of Solomon, the great Hebrew king, willingly paid him ________________.

5. Conscientious parents will do everything they can to foster and develop the ________________ intellectual curiosity of a small child.

6. Nutritionists say that most of us could ________________ on a great deal less food than we actually consume.

7. Authoritarian governments often resort to violence and coercion in their efforts to repress political ________________.

8. The wranglers suspected that there were wolves or mountain lions nearby when the herd suddenly grew nervous and ________________.

9. Our financial situations are so different that what she considers a mere ________________ seems a fortune to me.

10. Am I to be ________________ before the entire student body because I made a few minor mistakes as a member of the student council?

End Set A

Definitions

Note the spelling, pronunciation, part(s) of speech, and definition(s) of each of the following words. Then write the appropriate form of the word in the blank space in the illustrative sentence(s) following.

1. amenity (ə men′ ə tē)

(*n.*) that which is pleasant or agreeable; (*pl.*) attractive features, customs, etc.

When I backpack, there are certain basic ________________, such as hot meals and a dry tent, that I will not go without.

2. epicurean (ep ə kyü′ rē ən)

(*adj.*) devoted to the pursuit of pleasure; fond of good food, comfort, and ease; with discriminating tastes; (*n.*) a person with discriminating tastes

The chef took an ________________ delight in presenting the most delicious dishes to his demanding clientele.

Even the most fervent ________________ should not expect fine dining in a poor, war-torn country.

3. iniquity (i nik′ wə tē)

(*n.*) wickedness, sin; a grossly immoral act

English Puritans looked upon the court that surrounded King Charles I as a den of ________________.

4. inviolable (in vī′ ə lə bəl)

(*adj.*) sacred; of such a character that it must not be broken, injured, or profaned

Safeguarding the retirement income of millions of Americans is an ________________ trust of the federal government.

5. mutable (myü′ tə bəl)

(*adj.*) open to or capable of change, fickle

Most people would agree that one's principles and moral values should not be as ________________ as fashion.

6. panegyric (pan ə ji′ rik)

(*n.*) formal or elaborate praise; a tribute

The speaker delivered a ________________ in honor of the award-winning author.

7. presage (pres′ ij)

(*v.*) to foreshadow or point to a future event; to predict; (*n.*) a warning or indication of the future

The skirmishes at the border ________________ a war.

The fall in stock prices and retail sales may be a ________________ of hard economic times to come.

8. promulgate (präm′ əl gāt)

(*v.*) to proclaim or issue officially; to make known far and wide

The School Board ________________ a new approach to education that emphasized phonics.

9. rectitude (rek' tə tüd) (*n.*) uprightness, righteousness; correctness
The mayor is a person of unquestionable ______________.

10. seraphic (sə raf' ik) (*adj.*) angelic, heavenly, celestial
The artist painted the children in with ______________ smiles to suggest their innocence.

Using Context

*For each item, determine whether the **boldface** word from pages 218–219 makes sense in the context of the sentence. Circle the item numbers next to the six sentences in which the words are used correctly.*

1. The two competing businesses put aside their long-standing **iniquity** and formed an alliance when the large corporation began building an office in their territory that could displace them both.
2. The mother threatened to **promulgate** her offer to help with homework if the children did not clean up their rooms.
3. The **mutable** performance of this thoroughbred over the past few races makes predicting its odds of winning today very difficult.
4. As we saw the dark clouds on the horizon that normally **presage** a storm, we decided to turn the boat back toward the dock.
5. When I returned home after several days of camping, I appreciated every **amenity** in my house that I once took for granted, from the soft bed to the hot shower.
6. We would not even consider doing anything to hurt each other's feelings, as our respect for each other is **inviolable**.
7. He is a person of such **rectitude** that if he found a hundred dollars on the street, he would try to return it to its rightful owner or donate it to charity before ever considering keeping it for himself.
8. The **seraphic** look in her eyes indicated that she was just as bored with the conversation as I was.
9. His **epicurean** appetite is such that he hardly eats more than a bird would for most meals.
10. The beautifully filmed documentary about the wild-animal expert and her contributions to animal behavioral research was a moving **panegyric**.

Set B

Choosing the Right Word

*Select the **boldface** word that better completes each sentence. You might refer to the passage on pages 212–213 to see how most of these words are used in context. Note that the choices might be related forms of the Unit words.*

1. The new "gourmet" deli features delicacies that are bound to delight even the most exacting of (**epicurean, seraphic**) palates.

2. I hope that Jessie's obvious nervousness during the dress rehearsal does not (**presage, promulgate**) a poor performance in the play tonight.

3. "Angelica" is indeed an apt name for one whose (**mutable, seraphic**) beauty is complemented by such sweetness of temper and gentleness of spirit.

4. No matter how well defended, no boundary is (**inviolable, epicurean**) unless the people on either side of it respect one another.

5. The resounding victory we scored at the polls is an eloquent tribute to the (**rectitude, iniquity**) of her approach as campaign manager.

6. Specific customs vary widely in different lands, but the basic (**presages, amenities**) of civilized living are much the same everywhere.

7. The study of government shows us that many political institutions thought to be unchanging are in fact highly (**inviolable, mutable**).

8. Recently, the principal (**promulgated, presaged**) a new dress code that abolished some of the unnecessary strictness of the old rules.

9. Instead of being so concerned with the (**iniquities, rectitude**) of others, they would do well to concentrate on correcting their own shortcomings.

10. (**Panegyrics, Amenities**) at the luxury spa include massages and steam baths.

11. Instead of mouthing empty (**panegyrics, amenities**) to the Bill of Rights, let's strive to make this great document a reality in our lives.

12. Grandma sighed, "Kim's taste in clothes is so (**inviolable, mutable**) that nobody even tries to guess what she'll wear from week to week."

Completing the Sentence

Choose the word from the word bank that best completes each of the following sentences. Write the correct word or form of the word in the space provided.

amenity	**iniquity**	**mutable**	**presage**	**rectitude**
epicurean	**inviolable**	**panegyric**	**promulgate**	**seraphic**

1. Imagine someone with my ____________________ tastes having to live for a week on that watery mush!

2. I see no reason to question the ____________________ of her dealings with us since I know her to be "as honest as the day is long."

3. We are sure that their vow is ____________________ because their sense of moral obligation will prevent them from ever breaking it.

4. He inveighs against the sins of society with all the stridency of an Old Testament prophet castigating the ____________________ of the unworthy.

5. The biography is a pretty evenhanded appraisal of the man's strengths and weaknesses, not just another ____________________ to a great hero.

6. The President has ____________________ a policy that commits the nation to curbing pollution.

7. After a few days in which everything went my way, I suddenly learned just how ____________________ Lady Luck can be.

8. For many ancient peoples, the appearance of a comet was a fearful omen that ____________________ great social upheaval.

9. "I'm afraid that the child's ____________________ countenance belies the mischief in his heart," I observed sadly.

10. It was the ____________________ of its natural setting on those rolling hills that led the architect to dub the estate "Mount Pleasant."

End Set B

Synonyms

*Choose the word or form of the word from this Unit that is the same or most nearly the same in meaning as the **boldface** word or expression in the phrase. Write that word on the line. Use a dictionary if necessary.*

1. a hotel with every **convenience** __________
2. enter through the **small opening** __________
3. a **saintly** figure dressed in white __________
4. tried to **survive** in a desert __________
5. a **tribute** for a lifetime of achievement __________
6. the **sacrosanct** principle of equality __________
7. was **publicly criticized** for bad behavior __________
8. a **hedonistic** display of luxury __________
9. **fidgety** after the caffeine __________
10. paid **respect** to those who came before her __________
11. admired for maintaining his **integrity** __________
12. repaid a mere **modicum** of what is owed __________
13. dark clouds that **portend** rain __________
14. the angry **dissent** of protestors __________
15. showed a **budding** interest in politics __________

Antonyms

*Choose the word or form of the word from this Unit that is most nearly opposite in meaning to the **boldface** word or expression in the phrase. Write that word on the line. Use a dictionary if necessary.*

1. insulted the king's **ancestors** __________
2. a **thrifty** manager __________
3. will **withdraw** his decision __________
4. cast off for his **righteousness** __________
5. the government's **steadfast** policies __________

Writing: Words in Action

How might the experience of keeping a diary be different from composing an autobiography? Write a brief essay comparing and contrasting the two genres, and explain which kind of writing you would prefer to do. Use examples from your reading (refer to pages 212–213) and three or more words from this Unit.

Vocabulary in Context

Some of the words you have studied in this Unit appear in ***boldface*** *type. Read the passage below, and then circle the letter of the correct answer for each word as it is used in context.*

Margaret Hoby was born Margaret Dakins in 1571 in Derbeyshire, England. Hoby was well educated and married into a family closely associated with Queen Elizabeth I. After being widowed twice, she married Sir Thomas Posthumous Hoby in 1596. Not long after, in August 1599, Lady Hoby began a diary, which she wrote through August 1605. Her diary is one of the oldest known existing diaries written by an English woman. The diary gives modern scholars an **aperture** to view the day-to-day life and beliefs of an Elizabethan gentlewoman. By today's standards it seems impersonal, but the daily entries show her interest in her neighborhood, religion, and household. The diary was a place for her to record and reflect on her beliefs. The entries are rich with **panegyrics** and expressions of her **obeisance** to the Puritan way of life, with few notes of **dissidence**. When her mind is not on **seraphic** matters, she describes the crops growing in her area of northern England, the recreational games of wealthy Elizabethans that were to **presage** modern games, and the illnesses and injuries people of the day were prey to.

While Hoby's diary has ensured her name is still known, her husband, Sir Thomas Hoby, has remained part of the culture in a different and more public way. Puritans such as the Hobys were satirized relentlessly on the Elizabethan stage, and Sir Thomas Hoby is widely believed to have been the model for Malvolio, the absurd puritanical steward in Shakespeare's *Twelfth Night*.

---

1. An **aperture** is a(n)
a. tool
b. opening
c. unquestionable certainty
d. an imperative to lead

2. The word **panegyric** most nearly means
a. tribute
b. belief
c. complaint
d. gesture

3. To express **obeisance** is to show
a. knowledge
b. reservations
c. submission
d. acceptance

4. If you express **dissidence** you are
a. discontent
b. fearful
c. dishonest
d. disobedient

5. **Seraphic** matters are
a. false
b. inscrutable
c. dishonest
d. heavenly

6. To **presage** modern games is to
a. foreshadow or predict
b. provide a basis for
c. undermine
d. overwhelm

Vocabulary for Comprehension

Part 1

*Read this passage, which contains words in **boldface** that appear in Units 13–15. Then choose the best answer to each question based on what is stated or implied in the passage. You may refer to the passage as often as necessary.*

Questions 1–10 are based on the following passage.

Located in the Apostolic Palace in Vatican City, the Sistine Chapel is considered the **cynosure** of the Vatican Museum, with millions of visitors a year. The chapel's fame is due almost exclusively to what is inside: from floor to ceiling it is covered with one of the world's most famous Renaissance frescoes, painted by Michelangelo in the sixteenth century. These frescoes underwent a laborious restoration from 1980 to 1999. The Vatican raised money for the almost two-decades-long project, which cost around $25 million. Though it may be said that the Vatican was rather **improvident** in allotting funds for the project, this certainly was not the case if you consider the cultural significance of Michelangelo's work and the technical expertise needed in order to carry out such an endeavor. In fact, finding the right team of conservators can be a difficult process. The work of art restoration is far from **innate**. Like painting, it takes tremendous technical ability and knowledge. Patience is key in restoration: the first step in cleaning the frescoes was to delicately wash them with distilled water.

Before restoration started, art experts and conservators discussed just how far they should go to restore the paintings to their original appearance. Throughout the centuries, a variety of additions and repairs had been made to the illustrations. One group of fine art **epicureans** believed the work should be cleaned of any later alterations in order to bring to light the work as Michelangelo had intended it. Another camp of experts understood the subsequent additions as an integral part of the frescoes' history. While these concerns might seem like **minutiae** to the regular museumgoer, to people dedicated to art restoration they are part of a large and ongoing theoretical discussion in the field. What are the consequences of erasing centuries of dirt and alterations in order to bring a piece of art back to its original state? Furthermore, is it even possible to truly turn back the clock and restore a work of art to exactly as it once was?

How an expert chooses to answer these questions will depend on how she understands the role of restoration in the life of a work of art. During the restoration process of the chapel, sections were revealed to the public as they were completed, which brought about both praise and criticism. For some, the **ethereal** scenes shined more brilliantly than ever with the newly restored colors. Others, wanting to **gainsay** the positive opinion, argued that the shading and darker hues of the pre-restoration frescoes were more true to Michelangelo's vision for the **seraphic** illustrations. To them, the newly revealed tones made the figures look almost cartoonlike. Moreover, the restorers were even accused by some **captious** critics of using too strong a solvent to remove centuries-worth of grime. Everyone, however, agreed that the bright, vivid hues that emerged from the restoration painted a different image of the renowned Renaissance painter. Instead of concerning himself with dark, shadowy figures, he was more interested in exalting the human form by capturing it in brilliant colors. One could say, then, that restoration goes beyond mere cleaning and has the ability to shape the public and professional understanding of great artists.

1. The primary purpose of this passage is to
A) reveal how art restoration is complicated and controversial.
B) explain that the restoration of the Sistine Chapel was controversial.
C) provide information on how art conservators have the ability to erase the signs of time on any work of art with a combination of water and solvents.
D) argue that art conservators cannot agree on one way to restore works of fine art because the skills involved in restoration are so complex and hard to master.

2. As it is used in line 3, "cynosure" most nearly means
A) center of attention.
B) most famous room.
C) center of art.
D) most important room.

3. The purpose of the second paragraph (lines 28–50) is to
A) explain the first steps in the restoration of the Sistine Chapel.
B) express the complexity of restoration by outlining the different approaches.
C) show how certain conservators are concerned with only trivial details while others look at the larger picture.
D) establish the ability of an art conservator to change the appearance of an artwork.

4. In lines 45–50, the author most likely uses rhetorical questions in order to
A) reflect on the negative outcomes of restoring a valuable work of art.
B) express fear for the power that a conservator has to completely reimagine a work of art in the way that she sees fit.
C) question the ability of a conservator to erase the traces of history from art.
D) illustrate the types of theoretical questions a conservator asks before working on a piece of art.

5. As it is used in line 34, "epicureans" most nearly means
A) ascetics.
B) gourmets.
C) amateurs.
D) experts.

6. As it is used in line 61, "gainsay" most nearly means
A) question.
B) corroborate.
C) oppose.
D) accept.

7. According to the passage, what was the result of the Sistine Chapel restoration?
A) It created controversy among experts so people were unhappy with the result.
B) It revealed colors that changed the way experts viewed Michelangelo's work.
C) It ruined the frescoes by erasing the shadowing that was original to the work.
D) Even more people come to the Vatican Museum to see the cartoonlike images.

8. Which choice provides the best evidence for the answer to the previous question?
A) Lines 65–67 ("To them, . . .cartoonlike")
B) Lines 67–71 ("Moreover. . .grime")
C) Lines 71–74 ("Everyone,. . .painter")
D) Lines 75–78 ("Instead. . .colors")

9. The author's overall tone is
A) unfair to conservators who criticized the restoration.
B) impartial to both sides of the debate.
C) partial to the critics who preferred the pre-restoration chapel.
D) understanding of the Vatican's difficulty in choosing a restoration team.

10. It can reasonably be inferred that the more vivid colors revealed after the restoration
A) are more pleasing to view from the ground below.
B) were recreated by the conservators using the same pigments.
C) are closer to the Renaissance style.
D) complement the heavenly theme of the illustrations.

Vocabulary for Comprehension

Part 2

*Read this passage, which contains words in **boldface** that appear in Units 13–15. Then choose the best answer to each question based on what is stated or implied in the passage. You may refer to the passage as often as necessary.*

Questions 1–10 are based on the following passage.

The Louvre is undoubtedly Paris's most famous museum. While it is certainly known for its extensive art collection, including works such as Leonardo da Vinci's *Mona Lisa*, it is also renowned for the architecture of the building, which is arguably as emblematic of the city as the Eiffel Tower. Over the centuries, the Louvre has undergone many transformations, from medieval fortress to abandoned baroque palace and, finally, to revered museum of fine art. Yet, its most contemporary addition is famed for having **engendered** a great deal of controversy.

In 1983, the French president, Francois Mitterrand, commissioned the Chinese American architect, I. M. Pei, to work on a project to reorganize the Louvre. The result, completed in 1989, was a new 71-foot tall glass-paneled pyramid right in the center of the Cour Napoleon, the building's main courtyard. While Pei was accused of being recklessly **visionary**, he promised that the museum's new pyramidal entrance would lessen the overcrowding from the multitude of daily visitors. However, part of that plan was not only to add a new building but to reconceive the layout of the museum itself. It is true that there was strong **dissidence** between Mitterrand and the citizens of Paris over the new architectural plan for the Louvre. The French president decided to ignore the people's protests and move along with the proposed pyramid. Still, the Parisians were **loath** to accept the mere idea of the new structure, and for good reason.

The Cour Napoleon is located at the back end of the building, so today's visitors entering from the courtyard no longer experience the original museum entrance, the East Front, whose **facade**, with its row of fluted columns, is an exemplar of French classicism. In fact, most visitors will not ever see the East Front or realize it is there. As a result, the entire introductory experience to the museum has been reimagined with the creation of the Pyramid. Also, many critics believe the modernist pyramid to be **incongruous** with the classical style of the building that encircles it. While the architectural style of the Louvre is quintessentially Parisian, that of the new structure is more a reference to ancient Egypt. Its placement in the center of the courtyard has been critiqued as well. For many citygoers, the Cour Napoleon is one of the **inviolable** public spaces in Paris. To them it is **manifest** that the colossal transparent structure is nothing more than an eyesore clashing with the surrounding architecture.

Given the significance to the French people of both the museum and its surrounding public space, it seems careless that the government decided to continue with the controversial plans to conceptualize a new museum entryway. It is very possible, however, that the president was somewhat aware of the **mutable** tendencies of France's citizens. The Pyramid, along with the updated Louvre, opened on March 29, 1989. To the surprise of many, it was welcomed by the people of Paris with a shock of enthusiasm and respect. Today, the Pyramid has become just as iconic as the masterworks on display in the heart of the museum.

1. The primary purpose of the first paragraph
   A) is to compare the Louvre to the other major attractions in Paris.
   B) is to clarify that the Louvre has gone through many transformations.
   C) is to claim that the controversy is the most interesting thing about the Louvre.
   D) is to establish the historical and cultural significance of the Louvre controversy.

2. As it is used in line 23, "visionary" most nearly means
   A) impractical.
   B) unrealistic.
   C) uninspiring.
   D) incautious.

3. With lines 30–36, the author conveys
   A) Mitterand's respect for the difference of opinion over the Pyramid.
   B) Mitterand's disregard for the citizens' difference of opinion over the Pyramid.
   C) the citizens' role in the fate of the Cour Napoleon and the Louvre renovations.
   D) The citizens' distaste for the government of that time and for new architecture.

4. As it is used in line 43, "facade" most nearly means
   A) entrance.
   B) egress.
   C) exterior.
   D) doorway.

5. As it is used in line 59, "inviolable" most nearly means
   A) vulnerable.
   B) invulnerable.
   C) valuable.
   D) invaluable.

6. By describing the appearance of the Louvre and the Pyramid, the author
   A) includes interesting facts about them.
   B) shows how insignificant the Pyramid is.
   C) proves that the Pyramid is unlike any structure ever built.
   D) compares and contrasts the shapes and materials used to make the structures.

7. According to the passage, what was the main reason the citizens of Paris were not willing to accept the proposed Pyramid?
   A) They believed that the most important part of the museum was the East Front.
   B) They did not want to go all the way around the building for the new entrance.
   C) They were worried that it would outshine the older buildings.
   D) They thought the architecture of the new and old buildings would clash.

8. Which choice provides the best evidence for the answer to the previous question?
   A) Lines 39–45 ("The Cour. . .classicism")
   B) Lines 45–50 ("In fact. . . Pyramid")
   C) Lines 50–53 ("Also. . . encircles it")
   D) Lines 53–56 ("While. . . Egypt")

9. Which best summarizes the passage?
   A) The French had good reasons to dislike the Pyramid, but now they love it.
   B) The Pyramid has been the most important architectural change at the Louvre.
   C) Many French still believe that the Pyramid is an eyesore in a public space.
   D) The Pyramid marked a big architectural change for the city of Paris, but it did not overshadow other Parisian structures.

10. It can reasonably be inferred from the last paragraph (lines 64–79) that the author
   A) thought the president should have listened more to the citizens' opinions.
   B) believed the president had expected a positive outcome though so many people were against the plans.
   C) was shocked that the president did not choose another architect when people expressed their dislike for the Pyramid.
   D) had full faith in the president because it was clear that he knew the people of Paris would quickly change their minds.

Synonyms

*From the word bank below, choose the word that has the same or nearly the same meaning as the **boldface** word in each sentence and write it on the line. You will not use all of the words.*

beatific	**epicurean**	**mesmerize**	**putative**
cacophonous	**innate**	**mutable**	**restive**
captious	**inviolable**	**opprobrium**	**seraphic**
desiccated	**loath**	**presage**	**wizened**

1. The **dissonant** cawing of a large group of crows abruptly woke her from her sound sleep. _______________

2. The 105-year-old man had a **wrinkled** face, but otherwise he seemed remarkably young for his age. _______________

3. A groundhog can **foretell** an early or a normal arrival of spring if it sees its shadow on February 2. _______________

4. She may be my **supposed** rather than actual cousin, but I have thought of her as part of my family for as long as I can remember. _______________

5. The yellowed, **dehydrated** pages of the old book crumbled as he started to flip through them. _______________

6. It surprises me that digital devices such as tablets and smartphones have the power to **enthrall** very young children. _______________

7. No matter how **averse** you may be to the idea, you must admit that your vacation is over and it is time to go back to real life. _______________

8. The new international food market has something for everyone, including those with the most exotic and **discriminating** tastes. _______________

9. We will pack both lightweight clothing and sweaters for our trip, since the weather can be very **changeable** at this time of year. _______________

10. Two common **cherubic** images are angels shooting arrows and angels playing harps. _______________

11. Some people have a **congenital** sense of balance for sports such as skateboarding and surfing, while others have to practice to find their center of gravity. _______________

12. You cannot be a true innovator unless you are willing to put up with other people's skepticism and sometimes even **contempt**. _______________

Two-Word Completions

Select the pair of words that best completes the meaning of each of the following sentences.

1. The characters in Jane Austen novels display ________________ manners, obeying the ________________ of social conventions that range from how many consecutive waltzes a couple may dance to the type of tea that should be served to guests.

a. decorous … minutiae
b. abstruse … canards
c. beatific … manifests
d. ethereal … pariahs

2. Once the news broke, the public heaped so much ________________ on the head of the hapless city official that he soon found himself a veritable political ________________, even in his own party.

a. dissidence … amenity
b. efficacy … ghoul
c. euphemism … canard
d. opprobrium … pariah

3. As soon as the famous movie star walked into my shop, she became the ________________ of all eyes. Customers stopped what they were doing to stare at her as if ________________ by the spell of her celebrity.

a. cynosure … mesmerized
b. aperture … engendered
c. pillory … promulgated
d. moratorium … subsisted

4. At the demonstration in front of company headquarters, the protestor who ________________ to address the media described the layoffs as a hurtful ________________ to employee loyalty.

a. gainsaid … panegyric
b. manifested … obeisance
c. consigned … behemoth
d. deigned … affront

5. Disgruntled army officers and other ________________ elements in the society engineered the bloody ________________ that toppled the duly elected government a few months after it had taken office.

a. dissident … coup
b. visionary … pittance
c. restive … moratorium
d. contrite … nostrum

6. Behind the courtier's outward ________________ of decorous sloth there lurked the ________________ imagination of an inveterate opportunist, eager to capitalize on any windfall that came his way.

a. aperture … incongruous
b. chicanery … improvident
c. facade … febrile
d. cynosure … nascent

7. Any official who is genuinely concerned about the ________________ of his or her behavior while in public office will think twice before engaging in the kinds of political ________________ and backroom shenanigans that sometimes go on when a juicy government contract is up for grabs.

a. progeny … machinations
b. rectitude … chicanery
c. imminence … blandishments
d. iniquity … cognizance

Idioms

In the essay about writer Samuel Pepys and his diary (see pages 212–213), the author describes Pepys as "raking over the ashes" his major vices and sins. This saying is an idiom. The author means that in some diary entries Pepys returns to discuss and reflect on unpleasant events from his past.

An **idiom** is an expression that cannot be translated literally. You learn idioms in the same way that you learn many new words—by hearing or reading them in context. If you cannot understand an idiom from context clues, you may need to use an online or print dictionary to determine or confirm its meaning.

Choosing the Right Idiom

Read each sentence. Use context clues to figure out the meaning of each idiom in ***boldface****. Then write the letter of the definition for the idiom in the sentence.*

1. After two months of tense negotiations, the union decided to **throw in the towel** and went on strike. _______
2. Did you actually enjoy that movie, or did you just **jump on the bandwagon** because it received three Academy Awards? _______
3. The employees applauded their boss for keeping them **in the loop** about possible changes to the holiday delivery schedule. _______
4. Jones wants to remain **above the fray** when it comes to launching personal attacks on the other candidates. _______
5. Because the investment scheme was nothing but **smoke and mirrors**, hundreds of people lost their entire savings. _______
6. "I want to speak to the manager now," Melissa demanded, "so that I can get answers to all my questions **in one fell swoop**." _______
7. Because they are so **quick on the draw**, they have an excellent chance to win the obstacle race. _______
8. When the video game was released, the developer must have made money **hand over fist**. _______
9. The police are **barking up the wrong tree** if they think Joey broke the windows; he has an airtight alibi for the entire evening. _______
10. Avery won a full scholarship to the college of his choice, so he is **sitting pretty** for the next several years._______

a. believing the wrong explanation for something
b. having knowledge of something
c. all at once
d. trickery and deception
e. not involved in the argument or unpleasantness
f. admit failure or defeat
g. support something because it is popular
h. in a good situation
i. able to react quickly
j. rapidly and continuously

Classical Roots

vid, vis—to look, see

This root appears in **visionary** (page 207), which means "lacking in practicality" or, as a noun, "a dreamer or seer." Some other words based on this same root are listed below.

advisement	**providence**	**proviso**	**visitation**
envisage	**provident**	**visage**	**vista**

From the list of words above, choose the one that corresponds to each of the brief definitions below. Write the word in the blank space in the illustrative sentence below the definition. Use an online or print dictionary if necessary.

1. a conditional stipulation; an article or a clause in a contract that introduces a condition ("that which is foreseen")
They agreed to sign the deal, with the ________________ that we serve as witnesses.

2. divine guidance or care; a manifestation of such guidance
Despite hard times, or perhaps especially during hard times, people of faith put their trust in ________________.

3. a distinct view or prospect through an opening; an extensive mental view
As we rounded the bend, we suddenly beheld the most breathtaking ________________ of our trip.

4. to picture to oneself ("*see into*"); conceive of, especially as a future possibility
It is hard to ________________ a modern America made up entirely of small farmers.

5. a visit for the purpose of making an official inspection; an act of visiting; a severe punishment or affliction
Health specialists are meeting to discuss the possibility of a new ________________ of tuberculosis.

6. a face, countenance, appearance, look, aspect ("*that which is seen*")
The links of chains he carried, which signified his sins, gave Jacob Marley a frightening ________________.

7. a careful consideration ("*act of seeing to*")
The committee has agreed to take your most recent request under ________________.

8. providing for future needs or contingencies; thrifty, economical
It is our agency's mission to explore the most ________________ use of our natural resources.

FINAL MASTERY TEST

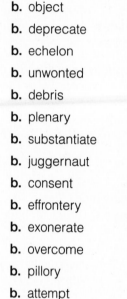

Synonyms

Select the two words or expressions that are most nearly the same in meaning.

1. a. abject	**b.** nefarious	**c.** wretched	**d.** fearless
2. a. jettison	**b.** object	**c.** volunteer	**d.** demur
3. a. decimate	**b.** deprecate	**c.** approve	**d.** deplore
4. a. objection	**b.** echelon	**c.** authorization	**d.** mandate
5. a. paltry	**b.** unwonted	**c.** beneficial	**d.** insignificant
6. a. flotsam	**b.** debris	**c.** frenzy	**d.** cabal
7. a. picayune	**b.** plenary	**c.** trifling	**d.** irrelevant
8. a. recant	**b.** substantiate	**c.** verify	**d.** amplify
9. a. eulogy	**b.** juggernaut	**c.** critique	**d.** tribute
10. a. fiat	**b.** consent	**c.** suppliant	**d.** decree
11. a. gall	**b.** effrontery	**c.** sophistry	**d.** desire
12. a. embellish	**b.** exonerate	**c.** countermand	**d.** repudiate
13. a. foreshadow	**b.** overcome	**c.** eschew	**d.** portend
14. a. renovate	**b.** pillory	**c.** demolish	**d.** raze
15. a. exhume	**b.** attempt	**c.** deign	**d.** stoop

Antonyms

Select the two words or expressions that are most nearly opposite in meaning.

16. a. apportion	**b.** presage	**c.** decry	**d.** commend
17. a. seraphic	**b.** feckless	**c.** effective	**d.** disagreeable
18. a. calumniate	**b.** hallow	**c.** embezzle	**d.** flatter
19. a. renounce	**b.** remain	**c.** delineate	**d.** arrogate
20. a. obsequious	**b.** youthful	**c.** thriving	**d.** moribund
21. a. forgo	**b.** consecrate	**c.** antagonize	**d.** conciliate
22. a. muddled	**b.** wizened	**c.** glorious	**d.** coherent
23. a. frenetic	**b.** calm	**c.** loquacious	**d.** vituperative
24. a. original	**b.** restive	**c.** militant	**d.** banal
25. a. moot	**b.** disturbed	**c.** intellectual	**d.** indisputable

Two-Word Completions

Select the pair of words that best completes the meaning of each of the following sentences.

26. His artistic choices are so strange and ____________ that he runs the risk of being labeled a ____________ and not being taken seriously.

a. eclectic … dilettante
b. rife … canard
c. pejorative … tyro
d. abstruse … progeny

27. The ____________ officeholder has a decided advantage over her opponent, who has never held office and is a political ____________.

a. visionary … effigy
b. felicitous … penitent
c. incumbent … neophyte
d. cognizant … utopia

28. I don't mean to ____________ the point by telling you again, but if you don't exercise, your muscles will ____________.

a. requite … saturate
b. belabor … atrophy
c. inure … mesmerize
d. loath … languish

29. It simply seems ____________ to ____________ someone for not throwing away a gum wrapper properly; wouldn't a warning be more appropriate?

a. furtive … vacillate
b. ebullient … congeal
c. aesthetic … discomfit
d. inane … incarcerate

30. My mother loves the simple life and has expressed many ____________ about people with a(n) ____________ lifestyle, but I think it might be nice to try!

a. facades … acquisitive
b. maelstroms … insatiable
c. animadversions … epicurean
d. shibboleths … sumptuous

31. The girl walked blithely down the ____________ path, unsure of where her ____________ would take her.

a. sylvan … peregrination
b. mordant … propinquity
c. taciturn … talisman
d. verdant … travesty

32. Though we all wrote anonymous stories to share with our creative writing class, I instantly recognized my best friend's ____________ style in the ____________ story set in a medieval dungeon.

a. laconic … overweening
b. ubiquitous … pertinacious
c. luminous … fatuous
d. macabre … ghoulish

Supplying Words in Context

To complete each sentence, select the best word from among the choices given. Not all words in the word bank will be used. You may modify the word form as necessary.

accost	**eschew**	**paucity**	**tenable**
allay	**illusory**	**pedantry**	**travesty**
bucolic	**murky**	**pusillanimous**	**undulate**
counterpart	**nuance**	**raiment**	**unremitting**

33. In order to lose weight, I will ________________ fats and sweets and eat more fruits and vegetables.

34. The teacher sought to ________________ our concerns about the upcoming test.

35. Our good fortune proved ________________, and we were soon back in deep difficulty.

36. The ocean water was so ________________ that we couldn't see our feet.

37. The subtle ________________ of this story will be lost on a reader who is less than attentive.

38. The verdant and ________________ setting was soothing in its tranquility.

carping	**echelon**	**garish**	**litany**
coterie	**emulate**	**glean**	**mundane**
dissemble	**enervate**	**invidious**	**nettle**
distraught	**gambit**	**jocular**	**stratagem**

39. The ________________ outfit stuck out in such a staid, somber setting.

40. The man was understandably ________________ when given the horrific news.

41. The constant ________________ of the children was beginning to drive the babysitter to her wits' end!

42. Lucius didn't need to say a word: I could ________________ from the look on his face that he wasn't happy.

43. Would he ________________, or would he tell the truth?

44. The pop singer's ________________ of admirers flattered her constantly and kept her shielded from criticism.

Word Associations

*Select the word or expression that best completes the meaning of the sentence or answers the question, with particular reference to the meaning of the word in **boldface** type.*

45. To **allege** that someone is guilty of a crime means that
- **a.** the charge is malicious
- **b.** an indictment will be handed down
- **c.** the person is clearly guilty
- **d.** the charge remains to be proved

46. Which advice would be most suitable for a person who is **recumbent**?
- **a.** "Grin and bear it."
- **b.** "Turn left at the first light."
- **c.** "Rise and shine!"
- **d.** "Keep your eye on the ball."

47. An **agnostic** will likely say
- **a.** "I don't know."
- **b.** "I believe."
- **c.** "My socks are always missing."
- **d.** "I'm running late."

48. **Histrionic** behavior is best suited to
- **a.** the laboratory
- **b.** the museum
- **c.** the stage
- **d.** the classroom

49. If you **temporize** when a decision is called for, you are
- **a.** stalling for time
- **b.** misjudging the situation
- **c.** losing your temper
- **d.** acting decisively

50. You would be well advised not to give **credence** to
- **a.** a reliable witness
- **b.** your creditors
- **c.** a habitual liar
- **d.** your friends

51. Typical **amenities** of urban life might include
- **a.** pedestrians on the street
- **b.** air pollution and litter
- **c.** museums and concerts
- **d.** bridges and cars

52. The wisest course of action when confronted by a **juggernaut** is to
- **a.** make up your mind
- **b.** stand your ground
- **c.** take its picture
- **d.** get out of its way

53. The **motif** of a play refers to its
- **a.** basic theme
- **b.** adaptation for television
- **c.** cast of characters
- **d.** financial backing

54. **Primordial** times occurred
- **a.** first
- **b.** in Ancient Greece
- **c.** during World War II
- **d.** as a result of negligence

55. A **figment** usually develops in
- **a.** an orchard
- **b.** the wild blue yonder
- **c.** a factory
- **d.** the human mind

56. In a **convivial** atmosphere, people may be expected to
- **a.** go into shock
- **b.** show off their erudition
- **c.** suffer from boredom
- **d.** enjoy themselves

Choosing the Right Meaning

Read each sentence carefully. Then select the item that best completes the statement below the sentence.

57. The knights had retreated into their **bastion**, where they hoped to regroup and repel the invaders' attack.

The word **bastion** most nearly means

a. facade **b.** aperture **c.** significance **d.** fortress

58. With books and clothes strewn everywhere, the bedroom was in a state of **disarray**.

The word **disarray** is best defined as

a. disorganization **b.** largesse **c.** paroxysm **d.** reconnaissance

59. The audience's **acclamation** was demonstrated by its repeated standing ovations.

The word **acclamation** most nearly means

a. asperity **b.** opprobrium **c.** victory **d.** approval

60. It was fun to watch the two puppies **cavort** in the field, dashing round and round the bushes and trees.

The word **cavort** most nearly means

a. rebuff **b.** gambol **c.** regret **d.** grouse

61. I would be extremely **chary** of taking up jogging again until the knee injury is completely healed.

The word **chary** most nearly means

a. bestial **b.** wary **c.** benign **d.** fecund

62. The critic's review turned into a **diatribe** against contemporary music in general.

The word **diatribe** most nearly means

a. tirade **b.** accusation **c.** surveillance **d.** badinage

63. Although the man did not plan the crime, his participation in the robbery attempt was evidence of his **complicity**.

The word **complicity** most nearly means

a. idiosyncrasy **b.** exigency **c.** animadversion **d.** collusion

64. I was able to guarantee his **collusion** by demonstrating that his participation would be to his benefit.

The word **collusion** most nearly means

a. detritus **b.** foible **c.** connivance **d.** chicanery

65. I appreciated the **celerity** with which the electricians responded to the power outage from the storm.

The best definition for the word **celerity** is

a. propinquity **b.** propriety **c.** verbiage **d.** promptness

The following is a list of all the words taught in the Units of this book. The number after each entry indicates the page on which the word is defined.

abject, 82
abrogate, 162
abstruse, 190
acclamation, 126
accost, 26
acquisitive, 18
acuity, 74
aesthetic, 174
affront, 194
agnostic, 86
allay, 106
allege, 118
ambient, 158
amenity, 218
animadversion, 30
aperture, 214
arrant, 114
arrogate, 14
askance, 150
asperity, 162
atrophy, 58
attenuate, 146
avid, 30

badinage, 118
banal, 14
bastion, 62
beatific, 202
behemoth, 206
belabor, 18
benign, 150
bestial, 106
blandishment, 202
brackish, 26
bucolic, 130
burnish, 158

cabal, 158
cacophonous, 206
calumniate, 130
canard, 194
captious, 190
carping, 18
cavil, 150
cavort, 42
celerity, 26
charlatan, 146
chary, 126
chicanery, 202
cognizant, 194
coherent, 14
collusion, 130
complicity, 86
conciliate, 114
concord, 58
congeal, 18
consign, 206
consummate, 62
contrite, 190
convivial, 102
coterie, 102
countermand, 118
counterpart, 106
coup, 202
credence, 38
cynosure, 194

decimate, 146
decorous, 190
decry, 42
defunct, 174
deign, 194
delectable, 162
delineate, 70
demur, 102
depraved, 74
deprecate, 158
derelict, 82
desiccated, 194
detritus, 162
devious, 30
diatribe, 82
dilettante, 126
disarray, 58
discomfit, 170
dissemble, 38
dissidence, 214
distraught, 42

ebullient, 158
echelon, 114
eclectic, 158
efficacy, 190
effigy, 86
effrontery, 106
embellish, 102
emulate, 14
encomium, 14
enervate, 74
engender, 190
ephemeral, 106
epicurean, 218
equity, 82
eschew, 18
esoteric, 70
espouse, 174
ethereal, 194
eulogy, 42
euphemism, 206
evince, 38
exacerbate, 114
exhume, 42
exigency, 62

facade, 190
fatuous, 118
febrile, 202
feckless, 38
fecund, 74
felicitous, 102
fetish, 174
fiat, 70
figment, 70
flaccid, 162
flotsam, 62
foible, 150
forgo, 146
fraught, 146
frenetic, 58
furtive, 106

gainsay, 206
gambit, 30
garish, 106
garner, 74
germane, 14
ghoulish, 190
glean, 62
gregarious, 170
grouse, 58

halcyon, 26
hallow, 70
hapless, 170
histrionic, 30

idiosyncrasy, 70
ignominy, 74
illusory, 102
imminent, 206
impeccable, 174
impecunious, 158
imperturbable, 126
importune, 170
improvident, 214
inane, 86

WORD LIST

incarcerate, 62
incendiary, 26
incongruous, 194
increment, 130
incumbent, 58
indictment, 86
indigent, 102
indubitable, 82
inexorable, 162
iniquity, 218
innate, 202
inordinate, 106
insatiable, 18
intermittent, 82
interpolate, 174
intransigent, 14
inure, 150
invidious, 18
inviolable, 218
irrefutable, 114
irreparable, 170

jettison, 107
jocular, 58
juggernaut, 118

lackadaisical, 118
laconic, 170
languish, 170
largesse, 18
litany, 114
loath, 206
ludicrous, 62
luminous, 150

macabre, 118
machination, 195
maelstrom, 26
mandate, 130
manifest, 206
mendacious, 174
mesmerize, 191
minutiae, 202
misanthrope, 102
moot, 86
moratorium, 207
mordant, 59
moribund, 162
motif, 86
mundane, 70
murky, 42
mutable, 218
myopic, 30

nadir, 174
nascent, 214
necromancer, 158
nefarious, 38
neophyte, 82
nettle, 62
nostrum, 202
nuance, 70

obeisance, 214
obsequious, 146
obtuse, 150
omnipresent, 170
onerous, 162
opprobrium, 191
oscillate, 146
overt, 26
overweening, 74

paltry, 130
panegyric, 218
pariah, 203
paroxysm, 126
paucity, 114
pecuniary, 63
pedantry, 126
pejorative, 26
penchant, 74
penitent, 146
peregrination, 130
peremptory, 150
perfunctory, 175
perspicacity, 82
pertinacious, 103
picayune, 103
pillory, 214
piquant, 42
pittance, 214
plaintive, 171
plenary, 86
portend, 118
presage, 218
primordial, 38
progeny, 214
promulgate, 218
propinquity, 38
propriety, 30
pusillanimous, 59
putative, 195

raiment, 107
raze, 114
rebuff, 147
recant, 119
reconnaissance, 14
reconnoiter, 151
rectitude, 219
recumbent, 63
redolent, 126
refulgent, 126
reputed, 71
requite, 175
restive, 215
rife, 159
rudiments, 163

sacrilege, 30
saturate, 115
saturnine, 115
sequester, 159
seraphic, 219
shambles, 147
shibboleth, 130
slough, 119
sophistry, 75
sporadic, 151
stratagem, 59
subsist, 215
substantiate, 15
substantive, 38
summarily, 31
sumptuous, 71
suppliant, 27
surveillance, 83
sylvan, 87

taciturn, 19
talisman, 31
tantamount, 171
temporize, 15
tenable, 19
testy, 83
travesty, 87
tyro, 127

ubiquitous, 75
undulate, 27
unremitting, 127
unwonted, 39
utopian, 42

vacillate, 131
verbiage, 43
verdant, 43
viscous, 39
visionary, 207
vituperative, 131

winnow, 163
wizened, 203

Affixes, 8
Context Clues, 7
Online Resources, 13, 14–15, 18–19, 22–23, 25, 26–27, 30–31, 34–35, 37, 38–39, 42–43, 46–47, 57, 58–59, 62–63, 66–67, 69, 70–71, 74–75, 78–79, 81, 82–83, 86–87, 90–91, 92–93, 94–95, 99, 101, 102–103, 106–107, 110–111, 113, 114–115, 118–119, 122–123, 125, 126–127, 130–131, 134–135, 136–137, 138–139, 143, 145, 146–147, 150–151, 154–155, 157, 158–159, 162–163, 166–167, 169, 170–171, 174–175, 178–179,180–181,182–183, 187, 189, 190–191, 194–195, 198–199, 201, 202–203, 206–207, 210–211, 213, 214–215, 218–219, 222–223, 224–225, 226–227, 231
Reading Passages, 12, 24, 36, 56, 68, 80, 100, 112, 124, 144, 156, 168, 188, 200, 212
Vocabulary and Reading, 9
Vocabulary for Comprehension, 48, 92, 136, 180, 224
Vocabulary in Context, 23, 35, 47, 67, 79, 91, 111, 123, 135, 155, 167, 179, 199, 211, 223
Vocabulary Strategies, 7
Word Structure, 8
Word Study,
- **Classical Roots**, 55, 99, 143, 187, 231
- **Denotation and Connotation**, 98, 186
- **Idioms**, 54, 142, 230